SIMPLIFIED
HOME
APPLIANCE
REPAIRS

SIMPLIFIED HOME APPLIANCE REPAIRS

Dan Browne

Holt, Rinehart and Winston   NEW YORK

Published simultaneously in Canada by Holt,
Rinehart and Winston of Canada, Limited.

Library of Congress Cataloging in Publication Data

Browne, Dan.
  Simplified home appliance repairs.

  Includes index.
  1. Household appliances, Electric—
Maintenance and repair—Amateurs'
manuals. I. Title.
TK9901.B793   643'.6   76-4732
ISBN Hardbound: 0-03-042636-7
ISBN Paperback: 0-03-015621-1

Designer: Madelaine Caldiero

Printed in the United States of America
10 9 8 7 6 5 4 3 2 1

For Debby

ACKNOWLEDGMENTS

My special thanks to Michael Porter, who took all the photographs and assisted me in every aspect of preparation for this book.

To the Bridge Refrigeration Corporation for permitting me to use their facilities and work on their machines, and for providing me with a wealth of information based on forty years of experience in repairing appliances of every kind.

To Kevin McCloskey, who did all the drawings, including a life-sized whale that was used on the wall of a firehouse rather than in this book.

CONTENTS

INTRODUCTION

Everyone I know has experienced an appliance malfunction at one time or another. Ordinarily it costs around $25 simply to have a serviceman examine the machine and tell you what is wrong. The cost of the actual repair will rarely be less than $50, and often more than twice that amount. Many an appliance owner, confronted with a sizable repair estimate, chooses to buy a new model, particularly if the machine is a few years old. (Many others will wish they had bought a replacement after the old machine has been repaired at an inflated cost.) This book provides an alternative to this expense-ridden and frustrating situation by enabling a totally inexperienced appliance owner to repair all malfunctions likely to be encountered in the six major home appliances—refrigerators, room air conditioners, washing machines, dishwashers, electric stoves, and automatic dryers. Whether prompted by inclination or economic necessity, anyone who uses this book to fix a machine will find that the procedures for diagnosing the ailment are easy to follow, the necessary tools are either already on hand or readily available at modest cost, and the actual repair is quite simple. In almost every instance the repair will take less than an hour, usually half that time.

No single book can deal with everything that might go wrong with every appliance from every manufacturer. The malfunctions presented are those that occur most frequently—in all probability the ones you will need to repair. I have personally performed every given procedure to confirm that it is the simplest and easiest way to repair a particular malfunction. These techniques are the same as those generally used by commercial establishments, but at times I have modified them so that the reader is not obliged to buy expensive commercial equipment.

It is advisable to read the entire chapter on the particular appliance you are concerned with before beginning any repair. To avoid repetition, certain information is given the first time the need for it arises and then omitted from the rest of the chapter. (For the same reason, I have placed certain repairs common to both refrigerators and room air conditioners in the earlier chapter on refrigerators, and omitted this repetitive information from the air conditioner chapter.)

Repairing smaller appliances is beyond the scope of this book, but the reader who has mastered the material presented here will find that much of it also pertains to smaller appliances. You should not feel apprehensive about tackling a toaster that doesn't toast, a vacuum cleaner that won't start, or any ailing appliance.

While writing this book, my six-year-old electric typewriter went on the blink, and I took it to a repair shop. The next afternoon the repairman called to tell me that my machine was a basket case and I would be wise to junk it. Since I had never repaired an electric typewriter and hadn't the slightest notion of what lay inside the case, I thought about buying a new one. However, I could not square this with my belief in self-reliance; so, swallowing my apprehension, I retrieved the machine, took it apart, and made the repairs. And I am still happily using it today. So I can empathize with someone who switches on an air conditioner on a hot summer day and gets no reaction or returns from a movie to find a flood under the washing machine. These unhappy moments needn't end in frustration and a significant outlay of money. Instead, they can provide the impetus toward self-reliance and competence in a certain area. For me, self-reliance is a process that begins with doing. If this book helps the reader "do it," it will have accomplished its purpose.

SIMPLIFIED
HOME
APPLIANCE
REPAIRS

1
BASIC TOOLS, MATERIALS, AND TESTING PROCEDURES

Most appliance repairs entail the replacement of a defective part. Usually the part is small and is attached to the machine by two or more screws with hexagonal heads. These screws are the sheet-metal type which are self-tapping—that is, they make their own threads as they pass through holes slightly smaller than their diameter. Figure 1 shows a *self-adjusting hex driver,* a type of screwdriver that adjusts automatically to fit screws of the various sizes most often encountered in appliances.

Bolts, or screws that are too small or large for the adjustable hex driver, are best handled by a *ratchet wrench* and interchangeable *sockets*. A wide assortment of wrench-and-socket sets is available in hardware stores. (Met-

ric sockets should be avoided, since they will rarely match American screw sizes.) Prices vary with quality, size, and number of pieces. The set represented in Figure 2 is perfectly adequate for appliance repair and costs under $10. One useful additional item in the set would be an *extension bar* for screws and bolts in otherwise inaccessible locations.

The *Phillips screw* is also frequently used in appliance attachments; it has an indented "plus" sign in its head. The screwdrivers represented in Figure 3 are appropriate for fastening and removing all Phillips screws found in appliances.

Figure 4 shows several types of *terminal connectors*. In electrical jargon, a terminal is that piece of an elec-

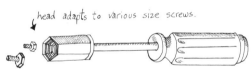

head adapts to various size screws.

FIGURE 1

FIGURE 2

Drive Ratchet Wrench and sockets

Extension Bar

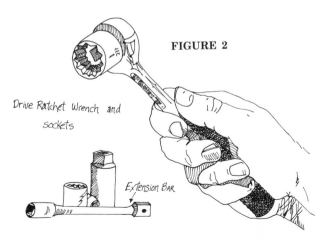

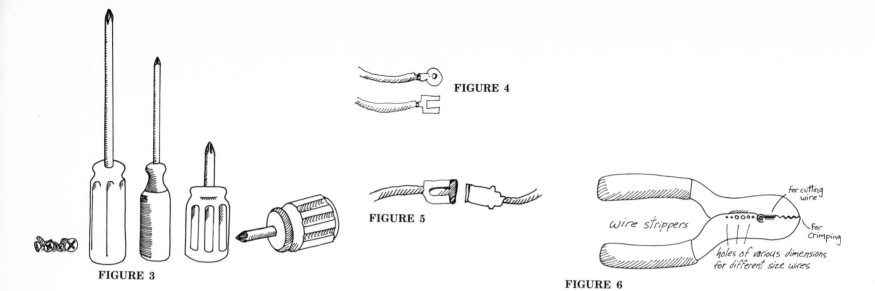

FIGURE 4

FIGURE 5

wire strippers

for cutting wire

for crimping

holes of various dimensions for different size wires

FIGURE 3

FIGURE 6

trical part to which wires are attached. These terminals are often prong-shaped, similar to the prongs on an ordinary plug, though much smaller. In order to connect the wire to the terminal, a connector is first fastened to the wire.

The *push-on connector* in Figure 5 is the most widely used type. It is pushed onto the prong to connect wire and prong. There is usually very little play (slack) in the connection, and some force must be used to get the connector on the prong. When removing this connection, it is good practice to jiggle the connector from side to side while pulling it off.

The multipurpose tool shown in Figure 6, called a *wire stripper,* cuts wire, strips insulation from a wire so it can be attached to a connector, and crimps the connector to the stripped portion of the wire.

For cutting, insert the wire between the jaws directly above the numbered holes and squeeze the jaws shut.

To strip insulation from the wire, it is first necessary to match the diameter of the copper in the wire with the diameter of the hole in the stripper. Each such hole is numbered according to the size of wire; the higher the number, the smaller the diameter of the copper in the wire. The size of the

wire is rarely marked (when it is, it will be printed on the insulation), and it is often necessary to guess by close-up comparison of the size of the copper and the hole in the stripper.

The size of wires used in appliance repair is usually #16 or higher. Only $\frac{1}{4}$ inch to $\frac{1}{2}$ inch of insulation should be removed from the end of the wire. Open the jaws of the stripper, place $\frac{1}{4}$ inch to $\frac{1}{2}$ inch of wire in the hole corresponding to the diameter of the copper, close the jaws, rotate the stripper for a couple of half-turns, and pull off the insulation.

If the hole was too small for the wire, the copper will most likely be nicked. This can easily cause a break later on. It is good practice to cut off the nicked piece, place the wire in the next larger hole, and restrip the end. Wire lengths are usually cut with enough slack so that removing a small amount will not leave the wire too short to use.

To attach the terminal connector, insert the stripped end of the wire into the tubular part of the connector, place the union between the outer, unsharpened part of the stripper's jaws, and press the jaws together. This indents, or crimps, the tubular portion against the wire inside and forms a satisfactory connection without the use of solder.

The *pigtail* (Figure 7) is an electrical testing device sold in hardware stores for under a dollar. It consists of a light bulb in an insulated holder with two wires (called *leads*) stripped of insulation at their ends.

A pigtail is commonly used to determine whether a wall outlet has electricity in it. This is done by holding the insulated portion of the leads and inserting the stripped ends into the two openings of the outlet. If the bulb lights, the outlet has electricity and is "live." If it doesn't light, no electricity is present; the outlet is "dead."

Another use of the pigtail is to determine whether electricity is present in a single wire. Figure 8 shows an ordinary switch used to control a light in house wiring. Many of the electrical parts in appliances perform similar functions by permitting electricity to flow through them when needed and to switch it off when a particular phase of operation is completed.

Two "incoming" wires enter the switch box from the power source. Two "outgoing" wires leave the switch box and continue to the light it controls. One wire in each pair is covered with white insulation, and the other wire with black. These wires are always separated from each other, although both may be contained within an outer sheath of insulation which makes them appear as one. The wires themselves are never joined to each other. The two wires, though always separate, work in conjunction with each other in a 110-volt system.

The black wire is called the *hot* or *live wire*. It carries the full 110 volts.

The white wire is called the *neutral* or *ground wire*. It literally ends up in the ground, attached either to a length of metal driven into the ground or to a cold-water-main pipe which proceeds underground to the

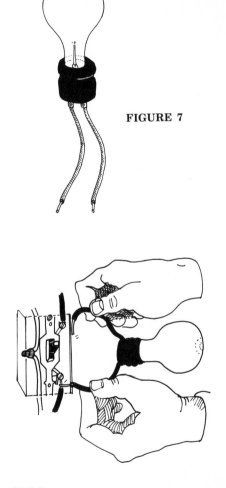

FIGURE 7

FIGURE 8

water supply system. (Driven and cold-water grounds are often used together to ground a house wiring system.)

Often there is also a third wire, a thin uninsulated copper wire inside the appliance cord or a separate green-colored insulated wire. Its purpose is safety, to prevent injury due to accidental shocks or shorts. The separate grounding wire is attached at one end to the green hex screw of the receptacle. Grounding an appliance is essential, but it is not part of the 110-volt system.

Electrical codes specify the colors used. White is always the neutral or ground wire. Black, or any other color except white or green, is the hot wire. Green is reserved for the grounding wire.

The white wire is *never* interrupted by a switch or fuse. It is continuous throughout the system. Only the black wire is interrupted by switches and other electrical parts in the appliance. Many of these parts may be considered and dealt with as an ordinary light switch.

In Figure 8, the white wire runs alongside the switch but is not connected to it in any way. Although the white wire must be attached to the aluminum-colored terminal of the light fixture if the light is to go on, it is the black wire that actually controls the flow of electricity to the fixture. When the switch is turned off, contacts inside it open, creating a gap in the path of the electricity. Conversely, when the switch is in the ON position, the contacts are closed, and electricity flows freely through the black wire to the fixture and illuminates the bulb.

The white wire may be cut in the box for convenience during installation, but it is then joined to another white wire and continues past the switch without interruption. The connection between the two wires is made with a solderless connector called a *wire nut*. To make such a

FIGURE 9

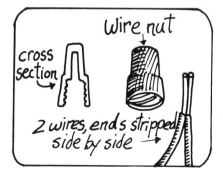

connection, the two wire ends are stripped to a length of $\frac{1}{2}$ inch, placed together, and the wire nut is then screwed down clockwise over the two (Figure 9).

In the electrical circuit shown in Figure 8, the incoming black wire is attached to one of the two terminals on the switch. The outgoing black wire is attached to the other terminal. In operation, the incoming black wire should always have electricity in it. To determine whether it does, place one lead of the pigtail on the incoming black-wire terminal and the other lead on the metal box in which the switch is housed. If the bulb lights, electricity is present; if it does not light, no electricity is being delivered from the power source. (The pigtail bulb will *not* light when one lead is on the white wire and the other on the metal box containing the switch.)

If the bulb lights, there may still not be current coming *out* of the box. Turn the switch "on" and place leads on the outgoing black wire terminal and on the metal box. If the bulb fails to light, then the switch is defective.

Although devices other than the pigtail will be used for testing electrical parts, their procedures are essentially the same—that is, no more

complicated than testing an ordinary
light switch.

The wall outlet into which the
appliance is plugged receives its electricity from the *main*: a metal box
into which electricity enters from the
utility company and from which it is
distributed and controlled around the
home. In a one-family house the main
will usually be found in the garage or
basement; in multiple dwellings or
apartments, it is usually in the
kitchen.

When an outlet is tested with the
pigtail and the bulb doesn't light, the
cause will almost always be found in
the main. There are two types of
main: *fuse* (Figure 10) and *circuit
breaker* (Figure 11). In the fuse type,
a disruption of current will be evident
in a "blown" fuse—the window of a
fuse will be discolored, with a burnt
appearance, or there will be a break
in the small wire beneath the window. In the breaker type of main,
one of the breakers (switches) will
have tripped to the OFF position. To
restore current through a fuse main,
replace the blown fuse with a fresh
one; with a breaker switch, push it
fully to the OFF position, then flip
it to ON.

There are situations where the cir-

FIGURE 10

FIGURE 11

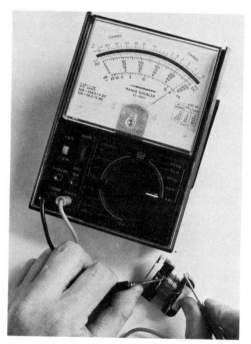

FIGURE 12

cuit breaker trips off again, or the fuse blows as soon as it is screwed in or after the appliance has been running a short time. These malfunctions will be dealt with in later chapters as they arise in particular appliances.

In order for an appliance to operate normally, electricity from the main must flow uninterruptedly through each of its electrical parts when needed and shut off when the function of those parts has been completed. Most malfunctions occur when an electrical part becomes defective and doesn't permit electricity to flow through it when the part is in its ON position. When any such "break" in the path occurs, *continuity* has been lost. Determining what has caused loss of continuity is a major part of appliance repair.

Since no electrical parts interrupt the continuity of the white wire, continuity testing is practiced solely on the black wire and on the electrical components that make up its path. It is possible to perform such continuity tests with the pigtail, but this can get unwieldy, and it requires that the appliance be plugged into a live outlet, with consequent risk of accidental shocks, shorts, and injury.

There are two readily available instruments far superior to the pigtail for continuity testing, and both totally eliminate the risk of accidental injury.

One such instrument is the battery-operated *multitester* (Figure 12), which costs approximately $21 and can be rented for $2 per day. It is reliable, easy to use, and, most important, *the appliance must never be plugged in when the instrument is used.* Since no power is being delivered to the appliance and the current from the batteries is too small to be felt, all risk of injury is avoided.

When electricity flows through a wire or an electrical component, that wire or component resists its flow. This is normal even when using such an excellent electrical conductor as copper. The multitester measures this *resistance* and indicates the amount on a scale as so many *ohms,* the units of electrical resistance. We are not, however, particularly interested in measuring amounts of resistance, but simply discovering whether or not continuity is present. *When there is no continuity, no resistance will be evidenced on the ohm scale. When continuity is present, resistance will be evi-*

denced on the ohm scale. We can therefore test electrical components and their wires and determine whether they are defective just by noting whether they evidence resistance.

Before using the instrument for continuity testing, *unplug the appliance cord from the wall outlet or other power source.*

The tester is equipped with two leads. Attached to one end of each lead is a plug, and to the other end, a probe. Insert the two plugs into the two holes (jacks) located in the lower-left corner of the tester's front panel. One hole is marked by a minus sign in a circle and the letters COM, the other by a plus sign in a circle and the letters vΩA (Ω, the Greek letter "omega," is the symbol for "ohm").

A red-tipped switch in the upper-left corner has two positions: vA/2, and below it, vΩA. Set the switch in the latter position.

On the right side below the scale is a selector switch. Turn it clockwise to the position marked RX1.

Place the two probes together. This will cause a deflection of the needle on the scale. If the needle comes to rest at a reading beyond zero, on the right half of the scale, rotate the red dial located between the letters OHMS and ADJ (adjustment) clockwise until the needle comes to rest at zero. Conversely, if the needle stops short of zero, turn the dial counterclockwise to bring the needle up to zero. The instrument is now ready to test for continuity.

Figure 13 shows an ordinary length of wire with its ends stripped of insulation. A probe of the tester is placed

against each wire end. If the needle deflects and comes to rest above zero, resistance is being evidenced, and therefore continuity is present. The wire is found to be all right.

If the needle does not deflect but remains at the infinity sign on the scale, no resistance is being evidenced and therefore continuity has been broken somewhere in the wire (although we cannot see the break through the insulation).

Many electrical parts in appliances will be tested in exactly this way, one probe on the incoming terminal and the other probe on the outgoing terminal. When no resistance is evidenced, the part will be deemed defective. When resistance is evidenced, the part will be deemed operational. (There are instances when this will not be true, to be described as they arise.)

Every appliance has attached to it a nameplate on which essential characteristics of the machine are specified. These include the *voltage* at which the machine should operate, usually 110 to 120 volts, though many machines require 220 to 240 volts. Voltage is the pressure of electricity, its force. As a rule of thumb, if the volt-

FIGURE 13

FIGURE 14

age being delivered to an appliance varies more than 10 percent from what is specified on the nameplate, the appliance will operate unsatisfactorily or not at all. Occasionally, it will be necessary to determine what the voltage is at the outlet supplying electricity to the appliance. The same tester that measures resistance will also measure voltage.

To measure voltage, the plugs should be in the same jacks as when testing resistance. Turn the selector switch clockwise to the position marked 250 v, located in the lower-right corner and lettered in red. Holding the probes by their insulated grips, insert them into the slots of the outlet being tested and read the voltage on the scale marked in red and labeled AC.

The multitester, excellent for determining continuity and voltage, cannot conduct a number of important tests that indicate what is wrong with an appliance. For example, suppose we have a refrigerator that is running but is not cooling satisfactorily. Continuity will exist in all components and the multitester will evidence this throughout, though obviously the refrigerator is defective. Another instrument, superior to the multitester,

FIGURE 15

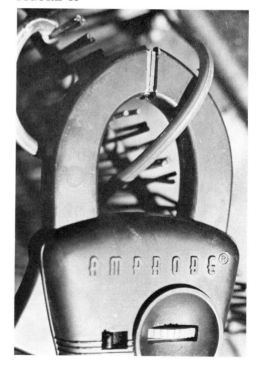

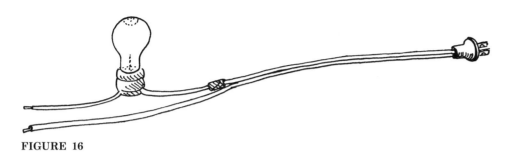

FIGURE 16

is available for diagnosing such malfunctions.

Figure 14 shows an *amprobe,* by far the most widely used instrument in appliance repair. It costs approximately $60.00 and rents for $2.50 per day. It is equipped with a small battery and leads for making continuity tests in the same way as the multitester. It can also measure voltage and watts. Its most useful feature, however, is its ability to measure *amperes.*

Amperes (amps) measure the amount of electricity drawn. Multiplied by volts, they give the amount of electricity consumed, or the *wattage*—for example, a machine drawing 5 amps using 110 volts consumes 550 watts. Electricity is metered and sold by the kilowatt hour (1,000 watts used for one hour).

The nameplate of the appliance states the amperage the motor should draw under normal usage. Let us say that 5 amps is given on the nameplate of the refrigerator that is operating unsatisfactorily. We now want to determine what amperage the motor is actually drawing.

To do this, it is first necessary to slit the appliance cord and separate the two wires in it *without* cutting the protective insulation around each. (The green grounding wire in the cord doesn't enter the picture.) Open the jaws of the amprobe and hang it on one of the wires, as pictured in Figure 15. It is important that only one loop be formed around the instrument since it will read double if two loops are made. There is a special plug, made for use with the amprobe, that allows you to hook the instrument

onto it without having to separate the wires in the appliance cord. In either case, with the amprobe attached, start the refrigerator.

Read the amp-scale needle. Let us say that it shows 7. This higher amperage indicates that the motor is laboring and requires more than its ordinary amount of electricity to function. So you can infer that some part of it is not operating properly.

Let us say that the amp reading is 3. When a refrigerator motor draws less than its normal amperage, it is doing less work. Inferentially, this is evidence of a loss of gas (refrigerant), since compressing a smaller amount of the gas requires less amperage.

The characteristic feature of the amprobe is its ability to test an appliance when the appliance is running and quickly provide readings that are a reliable indication of what is wrong.

When neither a multitester nor amprobe is available, the device pictured in Figure 16, a *test lamp,* can be assembled quickly and at little expense. It is used as a self-powered continuity tester.

To make the test lamp, start with a pigtail, a 5-foot length of ordinary two-wire insulated light cord, and a male plug. Attach the plug to the

FIGURE 17

wire by stripping both wires at one end for ¾ inch and wrapping each wire end clockwise around a terminal screw on the plug, then tightening the screw. Split the other end of the cord (making sure to keep undamaged insulation on both wires) and attach the end of one of the wires to one of the pigtail leads. Use a crimp-on connector and wrap the splice with electrician's tape to a thickness equal to the thickness of the insulation on the wire. You are now left with two wire ends, one from the pigtail and the other from the light wire.

To use the lamp tester on a wall switch, for example, place the switch in the "on" position. Plug the test lamp into an outlet and, holding the wire *only* where covered by insulation, place one wire end on the incoming terminal and the other on the outgoing terminal. If the test bulb lights, the switch is all right; if the bulb fails to light, the switch is defective. Electrical components in appliances may be tested in a similar manner to determine whether or not continuity is present.

A *buzzer tester* (Figure 17), which may also be used to test for continuity, can be purchased as a complete assembly in better hardware or

electrical-supply stores. It is battery-operated and sounds a buzzer when continuity is present. The appliance must be unplugged to use the instrument.

Its switch has three positions: OFF, T, and C. When the switch is in the T (test) position and the leads are placed together, a buzzer will sound to indicate that the batteries are providing current and that the tester itself has continuity. To test the light switch, place the *light* switch in the ON position, attach the ends of the leads to the two terminals on the switch, and shift the *tester* switch to the T position. If the wall switch is all right, the buzzer will sound. Here, continuity is shown by sound rather than light, as was done with the test lamp.

The buzzer tester has limited use. When the parts being tested have a relatively high resistance, as in the case of a heating element of an electric range, the current coming from the batteries and running through the

FIGURE 18

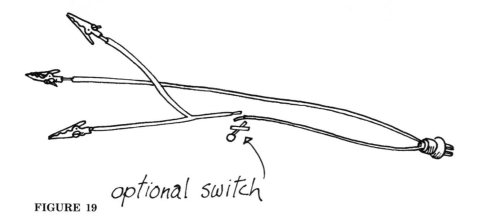

FIGURE 19   *optional switch*

Sometimes you may need to test a part in isolation from the rest of the appliance—e.g., to determine whether a motor will run or not. The direct-start cord pictured in Figure 19 is essentially an extension cord. One end has an ordinary male plug, and the other end alligator clips. To test the appliance, remove the leads from the motor terminals, attach the clips in their place, insert the plug into an outlet, turn the switch on, then quickly turn it off. If the motor starts, it works; if not, it is defective. Since power is coming directly to the motor, its failure to run can only mean that it is defective.

element is so weak that the buzzer will not sound, even though continuity is present in the functioning heating element.

Figure 18 pictures a device called an *alligator clip*. It provides a convenient way to make a temporary attachment to a terminal and is used in connection with a wire. The clip is attached to the stripped end of a wire by inserting the wire under the clip and through the upper hole. The end is then looped under and around the terminal screw of the clip and the screw is tightened. When both ends of the wire have an attached alligator clip, the device is called a *jumper*.

Jumpers are used frequently to bypass a particular component. For example, a wall switch can be tested by attaching the jumper to its incoming and outgoing terminals (and only then plugging in the tester). If the light now comes on, the switch is defective since the bulb lights when the switch controlling it is bypassed.

The tools and materials I have described to this point are those used in the repair of all appliances. They will perform most of the tests and repairs encountered, but not all of them. I will be detailing and illustrating additional tools and materials needed for each appliance as repairs on those appliances come up.

2
REFRIGERATORS

Home refrigerators came into wide-spread use after World War I, and for the next twenty years developed a deserved reputation for trouble-free operation over long periods of time. The reputation still prevails but is no longer as valid. The drive of manufacturers to lower their unit costs has led to the use of inferior materials, resulting in more frequent malfunctions.

A motor called the Meter Miser serves as an example of such deterioration of product. The first refrigerators to use it were scrapped long before the motor wore out. Twenty-five years of service was not at all uncommon. In time a slight change was made in the specifications of the motor—a new type of coating was used on its windings—and after five years or so, the coating began to flake. This contaminated the refrigerant system, and either the motor had to be replaced (though it still functioned perfectly well in other respects) or the unit had to be scrapped.

Similar examples are plentiful, and the proof is a vast appliance repair business. Today when you buy a refrigerator, or for that matter any home appliance, chances are that some malfunction will occur within a year, and after five years you will be thinking about trading it in for a new one as a less expensive alternative to continual repairs. With the introduction of such "convenience" features as frost-free operation, automatic ice-making, and blower systems, refrigerators have become even more prone to malfunctions. This situation applies especially to machines imported from the Far East, though is by no means limited to them.

As long as quality control rests exclusively with manufacturers, the situation is likely to continue. For the refrigerator owner, the choice is between spending a significant amount of money to keep the unit functioning satisfactorily or doing the repairs himself.

SITUATION A:
You open the refrigerator door and see that the ice cubes are melting or

melted. **Food feels warm. Water has collected at the bottom of the cabinet. You hear no sounds of a motor running.** *The light bulb is out.*

When you encounter the above situation, it is almost certain that the cause of the malfunction is minor in nature, easily determined, and quickly correctable at nominal cost. The key diagnostic symptom is the unlit bulb, evidence that *the entire refrigerator is not receiving electricity*. Refrigerator wiring is arranged in such a way that the light bulb will work even if all the other electrical components are out.

Of course the bulb may have burned out. To eliminate this possibility, unscrew the bulb and put in a new one. If the bulb now lights, you have a different problem and the material in the rest of this section does not apply. (Situation B deals with the same symptoms except for the bulb being lit.)

If the replacement bulb doesn't light, the reason why the refrigerator isn't operating is a *defective or unplugged appliance (lead-in) cord* or *something wrong with the house wiring*.

Check whether the appliance cord is firmly in the wall outlet. A "dead" refrigerator is sometimes one that is simply not plugged in.

If the cord is plugged in, the house wiring should now be checked since the likelihood of its failure is much greater than that of a defective cord. Unplug the cord, take a pigtail, and holding its leads by their insulation, insert one lead into each of the outlet slots.

If the bulb lights, power is present and the fault lies in the appliance cord. If the bulb doesn't light, check the main for a blown fuse or a tripped breaker. If that is the fault, replace the fuse or reset the breaker. In the situation we are dealing with, this will correct the problem in most instances.

If the breaker trips to OFF when you reset it, or the fuse blows as soon as you screw it in, there is a short in the house wiring which will have to be corrected by an electrician. Until the repair is made, the refrigerator can be operated from a live outlet on another circuit by using an extension cord of #14 wire or heavier.

If the fuse doesn't blow or the breaker doesn't trip off, retest the

outlet with a pigtail; the bulb should light. Plug in the refrigerator and the malfunction has been corrected.

If the pigtail bulb goes on at the initial test, either there is a defect in the appliance cord, or the malfunction is due to a loose or corroded connection inside the machine. To check the cord, unplug it, remove the contents of the refrigerator, and lay the refrigerator on its side with the door handle up.

With the refrigerator on its side, the box (Figure 20) that contains the ends of the appliance cord is easily accessible. One side of the box receives the plug coming from the motor. In the picture it has been partially removed for easier identification. Pull the plug completely out of the box.

To open the box and examine the appliance-cord wires inside, remove the hexagonal screw located in its center. This detaches the box from the wall of the refrigerator, though it is still being held by the wires entering and leaving.

In some refrigerators, removing this mounting screw will also separate the box housing from its back cover. In this particular machine, a needless tubular rivet in the center still

FIGURE 20

FIGURE 21

fastens the housing and back cover together. Removing the rivet in order to open the box is tedious, time-consuming, and often results in a cracked housing. A better alternative is to place the tip of a screwdriver against the rivet and in the gap between the housing and cover, then pry up gently. This causes a small break around the rivet inside the box and the box will come apart. It can be reinstalled later despite the crack, since the mounting screw alone is sufficient to hold the assembly together.

Figure 21 shows the opened box and the ends of the two wires in the appliance cord. The appliance cord contains three wires. The green grounding wire, which has a round prong at the plug end, is not attached to either prong in the box but is attached via a screw, as pictured in Figure 22, to the frame of the refrigerator. The ends of the remaining wires, one white (neutral), and one black (hot), are located inside the box. These are connected to other wires, and the connections should now be examined closely for looseness, breaks, corrosion, or carbonization. If any of these conditions is present, a rare occurrence, clip off the defective connection and replace with new con-

FIGURE 22

nectors attached by crimping. (Connectors are very cheap, and one should never try to free them from the wire they are attached to in order to reuse them.)

If the connections do not show any of the above defects, check for continuity in the appliance cord. Lay the plug end of the cord a foot or so from the box. Place one probe on either of the flat prongs of the plug and the other probe on either of the two terminals inside the box where the ends of the cord are attached. Figure 23 shows the cord being tested.

With two separate wires in the cord, the probe on the prong may be on the first wire while the probe in the box is on the second wire, and in that case no continuity will be evidenced. So if the needle doesn't deflect on the first test, leave one probe on the same terminal in the box and shift the other probe to the second flat prong. If the needle still doesn't deflect and come to rest at an ohm reading, the appliance cord is defective.

If continuity is evidenced on either the first or second test, shift the probes to the remaining prong and terminal. If the fault lies in the appliance cord, no continuity will be evi-

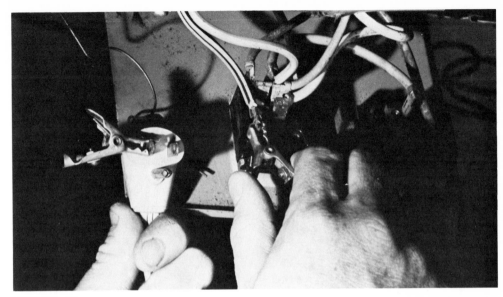

FIGURE 23

FIGURE 24

denced. *Both wires have to evidence continuity or the appliance cord is defective.*

The reading on this instrument when testing an appliance cord should be in the neighborhood of 1 ohm. Actually, the ohm reading on the scale is immaterial if one is testing for continuity only, but if a reading of, say, 500 ohms is obtained, this would indicate a partial break in the cord, even though the cord is maintaining continuity.

The larger the diameter of a conductor (the copper wire, in this case), the lower the resistance. When electricity flows through a wire that is almost broken, its path is restricted to the portion that is still continuous. Thus the normal effective diameter of the wire is reduced significantly, resulting in a resistance much greater than normal, as evidenced on the meter.

One should not attempt to repair an appliance cord unless the break itself is obvious. If it is, strip the ends of the break, splice them together with a connector, crimp it, and cover the joint with electrician's tape to a thickness equal to the thickness of the insulation on the wires. But the cost of an appliance cord is modest,

and the time and effort needed to locate and repair a break, or breaks, are usually too great to make such repairs worthwhile.

To remove the defective appliance cord, color-code its wires and the wires to which they are attached. Clip off the white wire and its connector. The black wire is already free. Strip $\frac{1}{4}$ inch to $\frac{1}{2}$ inch of insulation from the wires to which the white wire was attached.

The cord is still connected to the machine by a clamp located at the bottom rear. Remove the screw that holds the clamp and wire, and the cord will come free.

Purchase a new cord and two connectors identical to the ones that were clipped off. Attach them to the new appliance cord. Reconnect the already stripped white wires to the white wire connector by crimping, then lay the black wire and its terminal inside the groove in the box, behind the slot. Reconnect the box to the frame with the single screw through its center. Reattach the green grounding wire to the frame by the screw removed earlier. Reattach the cord to the clamp and frame with the single screw removed earlier. The replacement of the defective cord is complete.

Perfectly adequate appliance cords are sold in hardware stores and at a much cheaper price than cords sold at appliance-parts retail outlets. The connectors are also available and cost pennies. The plug end of an appliance cord is usually one-piece molded rubber, but this isn't essential and any three-pronged, 110-volt plug should be satisfactory.

SITUATION B:
You open the refrigerator door and see that the ice cubes are melting or melted. Food feels warm. Water has collected at the bottom of the cabinet. You hear no sounds of a motor running. *The light bulb is on.*

The light bulb is the key symptom. The fact that it is lit shows that electricity is being delivered to the unit. There is no need, therefore, to test the house wiring or appliance cord, since if either were defective no electricity could be delivered to the bulb.

When electricity is present in the unit but the refrigerant system isn't functioning (that is, the motor-compressor isn't running), the cause can be a defective thermostat, a thermostat with its control dial set in the OFF position, a defective relay, a de-

fective overload, or a defective motor-compressor. (There are other possibilities, such as a broken wire, but they occur so infrequently that only when all other possibilities have been investigated should these be looked into.)

The first thing to do is to check the position of the temperature-control dial (Figure 24). The dial is mounted on the shaft of the thermostat at the back of the cabinet liner (interior wall covering). A common practice in non-self-defrosting units is to turn the dial to the OFF position when defrosting. This cuts off electricity to the motor-compressor (but doesn't affect the light bulb). If the dial is in the OFF position, simply rotate it to the desired setting and the problem has been solved.

If the dial is in an "on" position (any of the numbers) and the unit does not operate, the cause is most likely a defective relay, one of the two most common refrigerator malfunctions. It can be corrected for less than $5 in only a few minutes.

The relay is contained in the pictured box (housing), located near the motor-compressor (see Figure 25). In some machines the box is accessible from the rear of the unit without disturbing any other component. If the

FIGURE 25

FIGURE 26

relay housing cannot be seen from the rear, or is difficult to get at, unplug the refrigerator, remove its contents, and lay it on its side with the door handle up. This provides easy access.

When a 110-volt current is applied to the motor-compressor, it travels through the relay coil to close its contacts. The motor's START winding is energized, the motor begins to rotate.

As the motor accelerates, the RUN winding current, or relay-coil current, decreases. This causes the relay's contacts to open. The motor continues to operate with only the RUN winding energized. The relay is defective if its contacts do not close when the motor is starting, or then do not open after the motor is running. The interval between these two moments is no more than a few seconds.

Relay failure can have a variety of causes. The most common cause in New York City, for example, is the cockroach. The warmth around the relay attracts cockroaches, they nest there, and their debris fouls the part.

The relay is mounted on a metal plate which in turn is attached to the motor housing. It is held by a single screw. Remove the screw. Lift the box from the plate and turn it over. It will be seen that the relay is held in its housing (protective cover) by a thin metal strap that runs through slots on opposite sides of the housing. To remove the strap, press the tip of a screwdriver against the flat end of the strap until it slides out of the slot. Lift out the relay.

Figure 26 shows a relay ready for testing. The relay has three flat prongs similiar to (though smaller than) those found on an ordinary plug. The prongs have wires attached with push-on connectors. Each wire has a different color and each must be attached to a certain prong—they are not interchangeable.

Although there are only three wires which have to be matched, it is sound practice to mark them and the prongs to which they are attached *before* any are removed. This may be done by marking each pair of prongs and wires the same color, or by marking each prong with the color of its wire. A good deal of possible confusion will be eliminated if this precaution is taken.

If a situation arises where there is doubt about where a particular wire should be attached, a handy reference is the wiring diagram attached to every appliance. It is color-coded; each wire is differently colored and the proper location of each is given in the diagram. However, these diagrams are often faded and hard to read, even when new, so the practice of marking connections *before* wires and parts are removed is still preferred.

Removed from its housing, the center of the relay looks like a spool of copper thread. Its ends are soldered to two of the three terminals. Remove the wire from either of the terminals to which the ends of the spool are soldered, and the relay is ready to be tested.

Prepare the multitester. Place a probe on each of the prongs to which the ends of the spool are soldered. If the needle deflects and comes to rest at about 5 ohms, continuity is evidenced and this first half of the test shows the relay to be all right. Conversely, if no continuity is obtained, the relay is defective.

If continuity is obtained, leave one probe in place and switch the other to the third terminal. If continuity is obtained, *the relay is defective*. If no continuity is obtained, leave the probe on the third terminal and switch the other to the first or second terminal, whichever has not as yet been tested with the third. Again, *if continuity is obtained, the relay is defective.*

Given the symptoms stated at the start of this section, it is most likely that the relay will be found defective.

When buying a replacement relay, it is wise though by no means essential to get one that is a duplicate of the defective relay. The necessary information is on the nameplate. To see it, lift off the bottom panel at the front of the refrigerator. (The pictured unit is a Hotpoint, of an early vintage. The location of the nameplate will vary with different units, but all refrigerators have a nameplate attached.) On the nameplate will be the unit's identification number. The Yellow Pages list appliance-parts retailers, and the identification number will be needed to get a duplicate relay. If a duplicate is not available, the supplier will undoubtedly have a substitute that will work equally well; you should not hesitate to use substitutes despite the admonitions of manufacturers. A huge amount of cannibalism exists in appliance repairs, and parts are interchanged continuously in commercial operations. Of course this can't be done indiscriminately, but then any reputable parts dealer is hardly likely to sell a relay for your machine knowing it isn't a viable substitute.

To install the new relay, attach the three push-on connectors to the relay's prongs, matching colors so that each wire is attached to the same prong as before. Lay the relay in its housing, slip the end of the strap through the side slot in the housing, and reattach the housing with a single screw to the plate on the motor.

If, on the other hand, the relay proves functional, another electrical part called the *overload* or *guardette* should be tested.

The overload is a heat-sensitive device used to protect the motor. If the motor is taking an abnormally long time to start, or draws an abnormally high amperage when running, heat inside the overload will cause its contacts to open the circuit. No current will flow to the motor and, of course, the motor will not run. When the heat has been dissipated, the contacts will again close the circuit, current is restored, and the motor begins to run. When this sequence repeats itself, the refrigerator is said to be cycling. The fault doesn't lie with the overload, which is simply doing its job of stopping the motor from running when excessive heat is present and allowing it to continue running when the heat

FIGURE 27

FIGURE 28

is down to normal. In our situation, however, the motor is not running at all, and this will occur if the overload is defective.

It can be defective in two ways: its contacts may fail to open the circuit when excessive heat is present, or they may remain open after the excessive heat dissipates. Since the motor is not running at all, it cannot be the former case, since this would provide continuity and the motor would run. If the overload is defective in the situation we are dealing with, it can only be that the overload is stuck in the open position, a malfunction that can be determined by a simple continuity test. To perform the test, we must first get at the overload.

The overload is usually located on top of the motor-compressor housing. Figure 27 shows its protective cover (which also covers the motor terminals).

To remove the cover and get at the overload, place a screwdriver tip against the lip of the cover on the side where wires enter, and apply pressure. The cover is held by its lip, which lies on each side under two small, slightly raised metal tabs attached to the motor housing. It will come free when its lip is pushed in from under the tabs.

Figure 28 shows the overload (and three motor terminals). The overload is held in place against the motor housing by a thin band of spring steel which curves around two of the motor terminals and the body of the overload. To remove the overload, press the ends of the spring steel band together so that they clear the two motor terminals, then lift out the band and overload.

The overload has two wires soldered to its terminals. Lift off the push-on connector for the wire coming from the relay. Prepare the multitester. Place a probe on each of the overload terminals. If the needle deflects and comes to rest around 1 ohm, the overload has continuity and is not responsible for the malfunction. If the needle remains at the infinity sign, the overload is defective.

To remove the defective overload, clip off its *wires and connectors.* Purchase a new overload. Two wires are already attached to its terminals. Strip the ends of the wires and attach connectors. Strip the clipped wires in the machine and attach them to the connectors in the same way the defective overload was attached. Replace the curved spring steel around the body of the overload, press its ends together, slide it down between the

motor terminals, and release the
ends. Slide the cover under the raised
tabs on the motor housing and the defective overload has been replaced.

If both the relay and overload have
been tested and found operational, the
motor should now be checked. It is
not the next likely item to have failed
but its terminals have already been
exposed and the feat is simple.

The three motor terminals pictured
in Figure 29 are marked with letters:
S for Start on the left, C for Common
at the Center, and R for Run on the
right. Prepare the multitester. Place
one probe on the C terminal and one
probe on the S terminal. If the starting mechanism of the motor is functioning, the needle will deflect and
come to rest around 15 ohms. If the
needle remains on the infinity sign,
the motor is defective and must be
replaced.

If the starting mechanism checks
out all right, shift the probe on the S
terminal to the R terminal and leave
the other probe on the C terminal. If
the needle deflects and comes to rest
around 8 or 9 ohms (a few ohms one
way or another are irrelevant), the
running part of the motor is functioning. Obtaining an ohm reading
does *not* necessarily mean that the
motor is functioning normally. It may

FIGURE 29

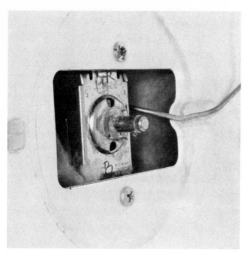

FIGURE 30

not be, but then the symptoms stated at the beginning of this section would be different. Also, a very high ohm reading is an indication that something is wrong with the motor in spite of the fact that it runs. In any case, the foregoing tests show only whether the motor will run, not whether it will run normally or abnormally.

Both the starting and running test must show continuity or the motor will not run and must be replaced. (Replacement of the motor is discussed on pages 46–47.) The motor itself (and compressor) is hermetically sealed. It is rare for even refrigeration companies to repair hermetically sealed units; almost always they are sent to the factory.

If the motor evidences continuity in both the starting and running positions, replace the cover over the terminals and overload and stand the refrigerator upright in order to test for the last remaining possibility—a defective thermostat.

A defective thermostat is a common occurrence. Usually it is evidenced by the inability of the thermostat to control temperatures while still retaining its continuity, but when the unit will not operate and the relay, overload, and motor are all tested and found to

be functional, it is almost certain that the thermostat has lost its continuity. In that case, electricity will be cut off from the motor-compressor and no refrigeration will occur.

In order to get at the thermostat for testing, remove the temperature-control dial by placing a screwdriver tip behind it and twisting *gently.* The dial is plastic and easily broken if excessive force is used. In many instances the dial can be removed by simply pulling it off.

With the dial removed, the two Phillips screws which hold the thermostat to the cabinet liner become visible (Figure 30). Unscrew both. The thermostat is now loose behind the liner. Turn it sideways and pull it from the cutout in the liner. Remove one of the two wires attached to the thermostat terminals.

The back of the dial has a half-moon-shaped hole (Figure 31). The shaft of the thermostat is also this shape and the two must be aligned before the dial can be placed back. (Most knobs on appliances are similarly shaped and can be positioned only when the flat portions are matched.)

Put the dial on the thermostat. Place the dial in any "on" position.

Prepare the multitester. Place a probe on each of the thermostat terminals. In all likelihood no continuity will be evidenced.

If continuity is evidenced, the only remaining possibility is that a wire between the different electrical parts tested has broken. The chance of such a break causing the malfunction is remote, but wires do become "crystallized" (brittle), and if the unit has been serviced just prior to the malfunction, the possibility of a broken wire becomes more likely; when a crystallized wire has been bent in the course of a servicing, it will often break. This type of break is usually located very close to a terminal. Wires soldered to overload terminals are particularly susceptible.

First, a close inspection should be made, paying particular attention to areas near terminals. If this proves unsuccessful, each wire will have to be tested for continuity. For the test to be effective, one end of each wire (and its connector) should be removed from its terminal before the probes of the multitester are placed in position on the wire ends. Fortunately the wiring of a refrigerator is easily accessible and not as extensive as in other appliances.

If the thermostat does prove defective, prepare to replace it by first marking its two wires and terminals so that a new thermostat can be installed with duplicated connections.

A long, thin length of metal tubing runs from the thermostat, continues around the freezer box (*evaporator*) and is attached at the rear of the box between two thin metal strips (*spacers*) held by two screws. This is the *feeler* of the thermostat, its temperature-sensitive element. The heads of the screws are inside the freezer compartment. Remove them and the entire thermostat is free to be lifted out.

Figure 32 shows the thermostat and feeler. (The feeler, also known as a capillary, has been bent into a circle for the photograph.)

Since the thermostat feeler is attached to the back of the evaporator between two spacer strips, installing a new thermostat is more involved than removing a defective one. The evaporator has to be moved out of the cabinet so that the new feeler can be attached to its back.

Along the perimeter of the cabinet are pieces of liner made of thin plastic (breaker strips). Insert a putty knife as shown in Figure 33 in the crack

FIGURE 31

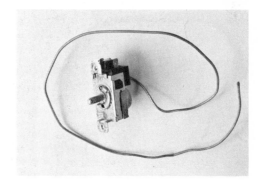

FIGURE 32

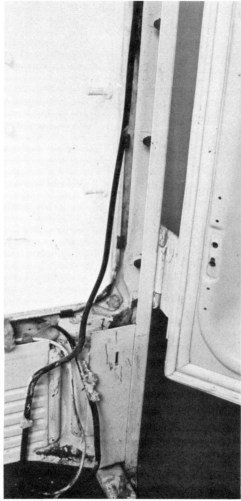

FIGURE 33   FIGURE 34   FIGURE 35

beside this trim, at the upper-right
portion of the cabinet. Gently twist
the knife outward until a portion of
the trim moves away from the retaining clips behind it. Continue
down the partially removed trim,
applying outward pressure at points
where it is still held, until the strip
comes away. Figure 34 shows the
strip removed and the retaining clips.

With the piece of trim removed, it
can be seen that the plastic-wrapped
tubing is actually two tubes: one $\frac{1}{8}$
inch in diameter, called a capillary
tube, and the other $\frac{1}{4}$-inch copper
tubing. Both emerge from the space
behind the trim through a molded depression in the liner and are attached
to the evaporator.

The evaporator is held in front by
two screws which go through its top
into two spacers on the liner above it.
Remove the two screws and pull the
evaporator and the attached tubing
out of the cabinet. (Prongs on the
evaporator at the back fit into two
extensions on the liner and support
it at the rear. There are no screws
fastening it at the back.)

Once the evaporator is out of the
cabinet (Figure 35), reattach the
feeler between the two metal strips
as pictured in Figure 36. In the photo

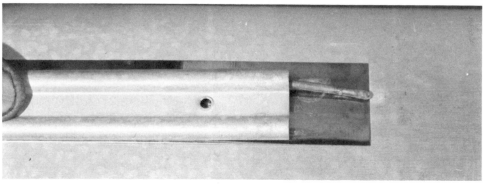

FIGURE 36

FIGURE 37

I have moved one of the strips in order to show the position of the feeler between them. In an actual installation, the ends of the strips are aligned.

After the feeler has been attached, push the evaporator back into the cabinet so that its prongs fit into the holes in the extensions mounted on the rear cabinet liner. Attach the front end of the evaporator with two screws into the extensions coming down from the top of the liner near the front edge of the evaporator.

Reattach the two wires by their push-on connectors to the two thermostat prong terminals.

Insert the thermostat into the cutout in the liner and align its two holes with the holes in the liner. Attach with the two Phillips screws removed earlier. Match the flat part of the control dial hub with the flat part of the thermostat shaft and push the dial on. The replacement of the defective thermostat is complete.

SITUATION C:
The light inside the refrigerator doesn't go on even with a new bulb.

This condition is invariably caused by a defective switch. The switch is a push-button type, usually located on the side of the cabinet near the top of the hinged edge of the door. The cylinder-shaped push button will normally be up when the refrigerator door is open. If it is not up, the switch is defective.

To remove the switch for replacement or testing, place a putty knife behind its flange (circular collar) and twist (Figure 37). This will pry the switch assembly out of its cutout in the liner (Figure 38).

As a first step in testing the switch, move each of the two wires attached to it to see if they are firmly connected. If one or both are loose, press the push-on connector(s) down on the terminal and the problem is solved. If the connections are tight, remove one of the wires.

Prepare the multitester and place a probe on each of the switch terminals. If there is no continuity, the switch is defective. To replace a defective switch, detach the second wire, purchase a new switch, reattach the push-on connectors to the switch terminals, push the assembly back into the liner cutout, and the replacement of the defective switch is complete.

SITUATION D:
The light bulb is on from the instant you open the door.

When the refrigerator door is shut, the push-button switch is depressed. This opens the switch contacts and no electricity is delivered to the bulb. The door must be opened at least three or four inches before the push-button can pop up, close the contacts of the switch, and deliver power to the bulb. To check whether this is happening, depress the button fully with the door open. If the light bulb doesn't go out, the switch is defective and must be replaced as detailed in the previous section.

SITUATION E:
Food and drink, particularly those items on the lower shelves, are markedly warmer than normal. You shift the temperature dial to the coldest setting but even after several hours, there is no appreciable change. You hear the motor compressor running without unusual sounds (such as hissing or clanking). *The ice cubes are completely solidified.*

Solidified ice cubes ordinarily indicate that the refrigerant system is itself operational. The problem must lie with one or more of several other possible causes: a faulty thermostat, a dirty condenser, poor door seal, excessive frost accumulation, or what oc-

curs most frequently, improper loading of food and drink in the cabinet.

A preliminary test of the thermostat should be made by turning it to the OFF position. If the unit continues to run, replace the thermostat as detailed previously.

If the unit does stop running when the thermostat is in the OFF position, the thermostat may still not be fully operational. Before other tests are performed on it, however, a look at the contents of the cabinet is in order, for overcrowding is a frequent cause of unsatisfactory operation.

Under normal conditions, there is a natural circulation of air inside the cabinet. The colder air around the evaporator falls toward the bottom, being heavier than the air elsewhere in the cabinet. At the same time, the hotter air given up by the food and drink stored in the cabinet rises to replace the colder air given off by the evaporator, for hot air flows to cold. This process repeats itself continuously and is the basis for the circulation of air in the cabinet. If the cabinet is loaded in such a way that the natural circulation of air is impeded or blocked, the refrigerating ability of the unit will decrease drastically, as will be most evident on the lower shelves of food.

FIGURE 38

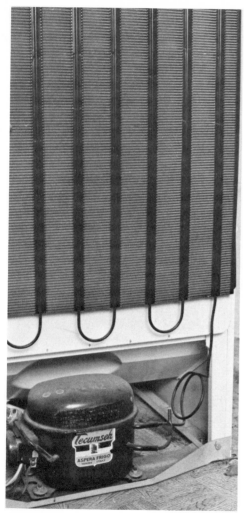

FIGURE 39

To avoid restricting the circulation of air, bulky packages should not be crammed against the rear wall. Spaces should be left between items on the shelves, and at least two or three inches should be left around the cabinet walls. It is important to remember that *not all* the space inside the cabinet is available for storage, and that once about 80 percent of it has been filled, additional items will reduce the cooling capacity of the unit to an unsatisfactory degree.

With the unit properly loaded, a continuing cooling problem may be due to a dirty condenser. Figure 39 pictures the condenser, which is fastened to the back of the refrigerator. As the hot refrigerant, Freon 12, passes through the condenser tubing, it surrenders a good deal of its heat to the surrounding air through the tubing walls and the "fins" (metal projections) attached to it. The hot air surrounding the condenser moves away naturally from the refrigerator toward the cooler air in the room. To allow free circulation of hot air from the condenser, several inches of clearance should be left around the back, sides, and top of the unit. If paper bags, rags, or any such items are stuffed into the gap between the

refrigerator and its adjacent walls or ceiling, the unit will not cool properly.

The condenser on a refrigerator is rarely seen and even more rarely cleaned. Animal hairs, grease, dirt, etc., accumulate on it and interfere with its heat transfer to the outside air. If the buildup is significant, less than satisfactory operation will result. Removal of such accumulated dirt with a bottle brush and vacuum cleaner will often correct the condition.

If it does not, if unsatisfactory cooling persists, further testing of the thermostat is called for.

Place a thermometer in a liquid that has been at the bottom of the cabinet for at least eight hours. Measured in the morning, the temperature should normally be between 35° and 40°F; in the afternoons, especially on a hot day with the unit getting heavy usage, the temperature can rise to 50°F. If temperatures higher than these are recorded, place the thermometer bulb into some ice cream in the freezer, or between packages of frozen food, and read the temperature after three minutes. It should be between −1°F and −13°F. (Different refrigerators have different lower limits.) If the temperatures are within this band, the cause of the unsatisfactory cooling is most likely to be leakage of room air into the refrigerator cabinet.

If the temperatures recorded in the freezer are five or more degrees higher than those given, unplug the machine and remove the control dial from the thermostat. On the face of the thermostat is a hole with arrows marked for greater or lesser cooling. In the hole is a screw, called the *adjustment screw* or *altitude screw.* In most models, one-eighth of a turn of the screw in a counterclockwise direction will increase the running time of the motor-compressor to result in a temperature drop in the food compartment of 2°F. Thermostats will vary with different manufacturers and different models, but all should be marked with the direction and amount to turn the screw to achieve a definite amount of cooling or warming.

Most often some such adjustment will correct the condition, but if it does not, reach behind the evaporator and feel the capillary tube (feeler). If it has come loose and touches the evaporator, higher temperature will result, since the feeler is recording

and reacting to the coldest place in the unit rather than the warmer surrounding air. The thermostat will be cutting off the motor-compressor before satisfactory cooling is achieved. To correct the condition, reposition the feeler between the spacers so that it *doesn't touch the evaporator.*

If this helps only partially, purchase a thicker spacer plate and position the feeler further from the evaporator. This will allow the refrigerant to achieve lower temperatures before the thermostat cuts out the motor-compressor.

If none of these possibilities is causing the inadequate cooling, then leakage of room air into the cabinet, and of cold air out of it when the door is closed, has to be the cause of the malfunction.

Figure 40 pictures the *gasket,* a piece of molded rubber that is mounted around the perimeter of the door and held in place by hex or Phillips screws. The screws become accessible when the flap of the gasket is raised, as pictured. With the door closed, the gasket normally provides a satisfactory seal between the air inside the refrigerator and the air outside. Leakage of air and consequently unsatisfactory cooling will occur if the

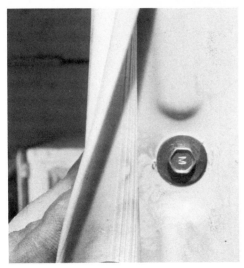

FIGURE 40

gasket has become defective or if the door has warped.

To check the gasket, first examine it for wear, deformations, tears, and so forth. If any such defects are present, take off the old gasket by removing the screws that attach it to the door and replace with a new gasket.

If the gasket appears sound, place a dollar bill against the gasket and close the door, holding on to the outside end of the bill. Try to slide the bill up and down, and to pull it out. Repeat this test at various points around the perimeter of the door. Resistance should be felt at every point. If there are spots where the bill can move freely, leakage is occurring there. Look at the spot and the gap will probably be visible. If one gap has developed, there will be others as well, and it is best to replace the gasket.

If the gap is a long one, or turns a corner, open the door and sight across it to see if it is deformed. If the door is warped, remove the two plastic covers located at the bottom corners of the door. Behind them are nuts to adjust the plane of the door by way of two braces behind the liner. When turned clockwise, the nut on the

bottom right will pull in the upper-left corner and the bottom-right corner. The other nut acts similarly on the other corners.

If the gap at the gasket is continuous, the door is positioned too far from the cabinet frame. To move it closer and create a seal with the gasket, first remove the cosmetic cover to the hinge.

The nut pictured under the cover (Figure 41) is for adjusting the door. There are two of them, one for the top and one for the bottom. Loosen both and shift the door so that the door and gasket are tight against the frame, then tighten the nuts. (Washers are available if needed to bring the door out.)

A last possible cause of unsatisfactory cooling (given the symptoms at the beginning of the section), is the excessive buildup of frost on the evaporator. The ice acts as a physical barrier, preventing the warmer air from reaching the colder evaporator. Natural circulation is restricted, and the efficiency of the unit is lowered markedly. All of us have seen evaporators with an accumulation of frost that reached the cabinet walls and prevented the freezer door from opening.

It is difficult to specify exactly when or how often defrosting should be done. It is a tedious chore, and even though the efficiency of the unit will go down as frost accumulates, up to a point one would rather take the decreased efficiency than repeated defrosting. A reasonable compromise, in my opinion, is to defrost the evaporator when the accumulation has become about $\frac{3}{8}$ inch thick.

SITUATION F:
Ice cubes are solid, food seems adequately cool, but there is a good deal of water at the bottom of the cabinet and on the inside walls.

Moisture in the cabinet is normal on a hot and humid day. Excessive moisture is mainly created by frequent door openings and aggravated by storing uncovered liquids (especially if the liquids are hot when placed in the refrigerator).

Each time the refrigerator door is opened, cold air, from which a good deal of moisture has already been condensed, slides out the bottom of the cabinet while hot, moist air rushes in at the top. Every time this is repeated, more moisture is condensed and adds to the accumulation

of water. If door openings are kept to
a minimum, the amount of water inside the cabinet will be reduced,
though perhaps not eliminated en-
tirely.

Further reduction in the amount of
water in the cabinet can be effected
by covering liquids before storage,
and by first allowing hot liquids to
cool to room temperature.

SITUATION G:
There is a persistent smell inside the
refrigerator. You have emptied it of
rotting food, and so forth, and washed
the liner thoroughly, but the smell will
not go away.

A washing solution of a couple of
tablespoons of baking soda in warm
water will usually remove odors.
When this fails, remove the plastic
trim around the bottom with a putty
knife, revealing the insulation behind
the strip. Spilled liquids can seep
through the joints of the plastic strip
and soak into the insulation. In the
colder temperatures of the insulation,
the metabolism of microorganisms
can slow down to a point where they
live on for months and continue to
produce odors. To eliminate the odors,
remove the discolored insulation and

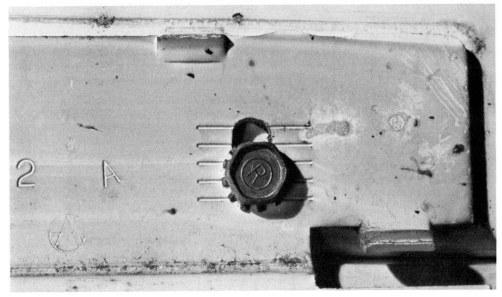

FIGURE 41

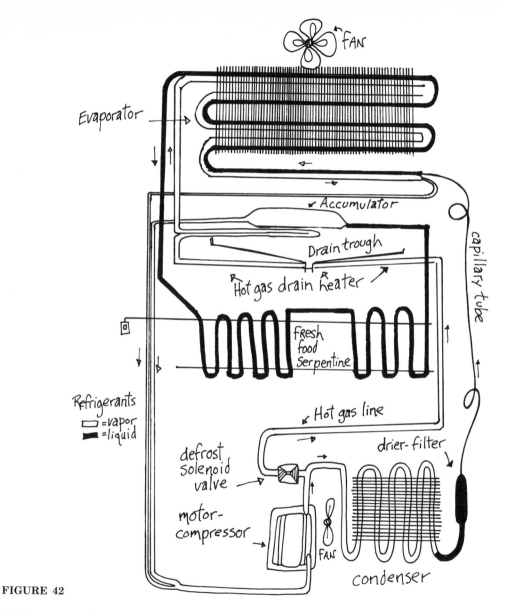

Evaporator

FAN

Accumulator

Drain trough

Hot gas drain heater

capillary tube

Fresh food serpentine

Refrigerants
☐ = vapor
■ = liquid

Hot gas line

drier-filter

defrost solenoid valve

motor-compressor

FAN

condenser

FIGURE 42

replace it with new fiberglass. If this helps only partially, remove the other pieces of trim and check the insulation behind them for discoloration and odor. Replace where necessary. (Neither removal of contaminated insulation nor washing with baking soda will get rid of the odor of a broken egg that has been allowed to remain in the cabinet for a week or two. I know of no way to eliminate this particular odor.)

SITUATION H:

1. **Ice cubes are melting or have melted. You hear the motor-compressor run intermittently. There is nothing wrong with the thermostat or overload.**

2. **Food freezes for a while in the cabinet, then it thaws and gets warmer than normal. Part of the evaporator has no frost. You hear the motor-compressor run much longer than normal.**

3. **You hear hissing noises each time the motor-compressor starts. There is no refrigeration.**

4. **You see oil on the floor under the refrigerator.**

Any of these four sets of symptoms evidences a partial or complete loss of

Freon 12 (dichlorodifluoromethane), the sometimes-liquid, sometimes-gas chemical used almost universally as the refrigerant in household machines. (The following information and procedures for dealing with refrigeration malfunctions are equally applicable to all types of room air conditioners.)

Figure 42 represents a typical refrigerant system with automatic defrost. Hermetically sealed so that no outside air may enter or any Freon 12 escape, it consists of an electric *motor* driving a *compressor* (Figure 43), which acts on the low-pressure Freon gas sucked in from the evaporator. After compressing the sucked-in gas, the compressor pumps it into the *condenser* (Figure 44). There the heat produced during compression (and from food storage) is removed, and the Freon is cooled and transformed from a gaseous to a liquid state.

On leaving the condenser, the Freon passes through a *drier-filter* (molecular sieve). The drier-filter (Figure 45) consists of a fine mesh screen and silica gel pellets inside a copper container. Its purpose is to absorb moisture and foreign matter in the Freon. From the drier, the liquid Freon passes through a long, very

FIGURE 43

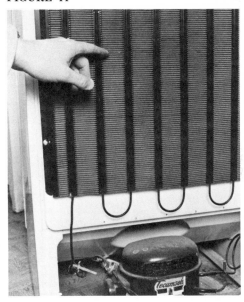

FIGURE 44

FIGURE 45

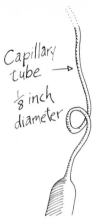

Capillary
tube →
⅛ inch
diameter

FIGURE 46

narrow tube called a *capillary* (Figure 46).

At the end of the capillary is the larger tubing of the *evaporator*. Figure 47 shows the joint between the evaporator and capillary tubing. The sudden emergence into the much larger evaporator tubing puts the liquid Freon under less pressure and allows it to evaporate (boil) and change its state back to a gas. This occurs at a relatively cold temperature. The heat necessary to cause the Freon to boil is absorbed from the air

and food in the cabinet, and the reaction from the Freon tubing provides the desired cooling.

When the Freon first leaves the evaporator, part of it may be liquid. Since the compressor cannot compress liquids, and indeed may suffer damage if liquid Freon is admitted, an *accumulator* (Figure 48) is placed in the line. This acts simply as a holding chamber for liquid Freon. While the liquid contained in it evaporates, the compressor sucks in the vaporized Freon and the refrigerant cycle starts over again.

The system operates under two pressures. From the discharge side of the compressor to the end of the capillary, the pressure averages 90 to 100 pounds per square inch. This pressure is referred to as the *high side*. From the time it leaves the capillary until it is sucked into the compressor on the inlet side, the Freon operates between 3 to 9 pounds per square inch. This pressure is called the *low side*.

Most losses of Freon are due to accidental punctures in the evaporator made while defrosting with an ice pick or knife, or to metal fatigue, particularly around joints in the tubing.

The latter kind of leak may be tiny and require months before a loss of gas becomes noticeable. Excessively long running time of the motor-compressor and simultaneous loss of satisfactory cooling are some of the symptoms. The loss of cooling may be preceded by temperatures actually colder than normal.

For any of the symptoms given at the beginning of this section, or if for any reason you suspect that something is wrong with the refrigerant system, hang the amprobe on one of the appliance-cord wires and compare the amperage draw of the motor-compressor with the amperage draw stated on the nameplate. If the amprobe's reading is higher than the nameplate number, say 7 rather than 5, the motor is laboring and should be replaced. If the reading on the amprobe is lower, say 3 rather than 5, a loss of Freon has occurred.

The first step in repairing a refrigerant leak is to find the leak. There are three methods of doing this: using the flame of a Halide torch, which changes color in the presence of even small amounts of Freon; using an electronic leak detector; or with a soap-and-water solution. Because most commercial refrigeration repair companies operate with some Freon in the workshop, Halide torches and electronic leak detectors are rarely used. Half a teaspoon of soap powder in a glass of water is the simplest, cheapest method. The solution is brushed onto areas suspected of leakage and any formation of bubbles pro vides evidence of a puncture.

There will often be oil in the area where leaks occur. Examine the oil, and if it contains amber or dark flecks, do not attempt to repair the leak. Such flecks are evidence of contamination from the motor, which would continue after the leak has been repaired. The motor-compressor must be replaced.

If the leak is in the evaporator or along the aluminum tubing, the hole can be plugged satisfactorily either by brazing or with an epoxylike product called Heat Stik.

Brazing is superior since the repair will be as strong as or stronger than the surrounding area. However, it requires an acetylene torch. A number of manufacturers have recently introduced acetylene welding kits, which are adequate for home repairs. They retail for under $30.

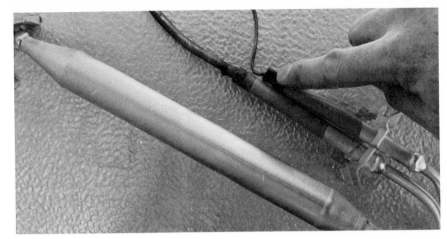

FIGURE 47

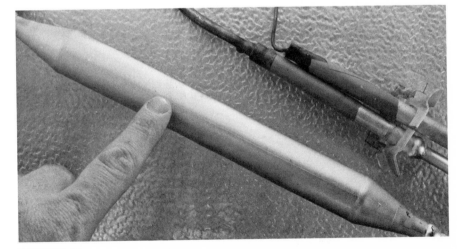

FIGURE 48

FIGURE 49

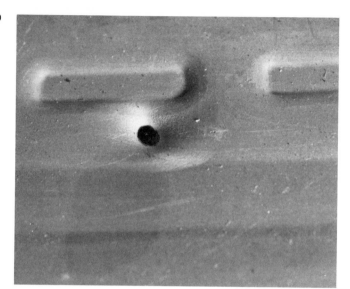

FIGURE 50

FIGURE 51

Figure 49 shows a hole in the evaporator. To repair it by brazing, the area around the hole must first be cleaned thoroughly. A small wire brush on a drill (as in Figure 50) can do the job best. The film that coats the surface on the aluminum must be removed and the metal rubbed with an abrasive until it is shiny. All traces of oil must be blotted away.

Figure 51 shows a Eutectic Aluminum brazing rod, which provides the metal solder to fill the puncture. It is used with aluminum flux, a chemical which cleans the area to be repaired while the brazing takes place and which is essential for a proper bond.

The flame of the torch, as pictured, is directed on the cleaned area for a few seconds until the color of the aluminum develops a yellowish glow. It is essential that the area not be overheated. If it is, the puncture will be enlarged and bonding will be all the more difficult. Just as the aluminum tubing begins to glow, turn the flame momentarily onto the end of the aluminum rod. This heated end of the rod is then dipped into the flux. (The heat allows the flux better adhesion to the rod, making it easier to transfer the flux to the repair area.) The flame is then returned to the

punctured area with the tip of the rod held close to it so that both are being heated simultaneously. When tubing and rod are both glowing and *just* as they both achieve plasticity, the molten tip of the rod is placed on the puncture and metal is deposited. The flame should *not* be held steadily on the repair, since this is bound to cause overheating; instead it should be applied sporadically, just enough to keep the metal barely flowing. Gently rotating the rod between the fingers helps keep temperatures even while directing the barely molten metal from the rod. The repair is started around the edges of the puncture and proceeds inward toward the center.

After brazing, the surface should be rubbed with steel wool to remove the crust and the weld should be examined for dark specks. These indicate impurities in the repair and a probable leak. If any are present, the repair should be redone.

It is essential that the brazing be done as quickly as possible since prolonged heating increases the possibility of contaminating the system. To braze aluminum requires a knack (it is much more difficult than brazing copper or steel), with speed highly desirable. I suggest practicing on a

scrap of aluminum to master the technique before attempting a repair.

An alternative to brazing for repairing a leak in aluminum is the use of Heat Stik. An area an inch or so around the puncture should be cleaned and made shiny as previously described.

The area to be repaired is only *warmed* when Heat Stik is used. For this an ordinary propane torch is satisfactory. Direct the flame on the repair area *briefly*. Heating the aluminum until it changes color is needless and undesirable. Place the Heat Stik alongside the puncture (Figure 52) and warm it until it just begins to melt, moving the flame in or out just enough to keep the stik at a heavy, plastic consistency. Spread it over the cleaned area and work inward toward the center of the hole. Keep the entire mass in a slightly sticky state by playing the flame over the whole area.

A repair made with Heat Stik requires little skill. It is a cheap alternative and needs only an ordinary, modestly priced propane torch. Some commercial refrigeration repair companies use it regularly, though all prefer brazing.

There is no question that the

FIGURE 52

brazed repair is superior. If done properly, the leak will be stopped for good. Heat Stik repairs have usually proven just as effective, but it is also true that failures of Heat Stik repairs occur more frequently.

If the leak occurs in the condenser or copper tubing, the repair is made with silver solder and acetylene torch. The solder should contain a minimum of 35 percent silver and should be used with silver solder flux. An area an inch or so around the leak is cleaned and made shiny. Any oil on the surface is blotted away with a clean rag. The flame is directed over and around the hole. As soon as a glow occurs, heat the end of the solder briefly, stick it into the flux, and apply it to the periphery of the repair area. *Do not* direct the flame at the solder, but lay the solder against the copper so that the heat built up in the copper melts the solder. The area must not be overheated, as would be indicated by the solder flowing too quickly. Controlling the temperature as the solder is being applied is critical for a good bond. When the glow of the metal becomes too intense or the solder runs too quickly, shift the flame away from the area. Even

though the hole may be only the diameter of a hair, it is good practice to spread the solder over the entire cleaned area.

If the leak is between the copper tubing and the steel condenser, the area is cleaned in the same way but the flame is directed only at the *copper*. This is the reverse of ordinary soldering and is necessary because the condenser steel is very thin and will overheat if the flame is directed at it, or at both the copper and steel simultaneously. Nor will there be a satisfactory bond if the steel is hotter than the copper, since both metals must be at the same temperature for the bond to be effective. By heating the copper, enough heat is transferred to the steel to make a good bond. Again, the flame is not directed at the silver solder. Melting is obtained by laying the solder against the heated metal.

In the course of searching for leaks, it will be necessary at times to gain access to the refrigerant system.

When the lower panel at the front of the refrigerator is lifted off, a small metal plate will be seen in the right corner. Remove the two screws which hold the panel, revealing part of the refrigerant tubing (Figure 53). Remove the breaker strip (trim) along the right side of the cabinet. Then remove the two screws that hold up the front of the evaporator. Pull the evaporator forward so that its rear prongs leave their supports at the back. The evaporator and its attached tubing (which lies behind the liner and trim) can now be pulled forward so that the entire refrigerant system at the front of the machine can be examined for leaks from all sides.

If necessary, the entire refrigerant system can be separated from the rest of the refrigerator without severing anything. To do this, remove the two upper screws that hold the condenser to the back of the refrigerator. Loosen a second pair of screws near the bottom of the condenser. Unplug the lead from the motor to the outlet box located under the machine. Swing the motor-compresser and condenser out from under the machine (see Figure 54). Tilt up the right side of the refrigerator and swing the evaporator and attached tubing out from under the box. The entire refrigerant system has now been separated from the rest of the unit and is accessible for leak testing with soap solution.

FIGURE 53

FIGURE 54

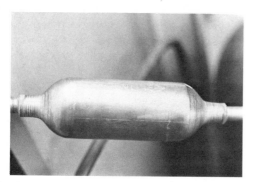

FIGURE 55

If a leak is found in the capillary tube, do not attempt to close the hole by brazing. Using the edge of a three-cornered file, score two complete rings around the tubing, each about $\frac{1}{2}$ inch on either side of the hole. *Do not file completely through the capillary.* Grip the capillary on both sides of one scored ring and bend the tubing back and forth to break it. Repeat this at the second scored ring. The tubing should break cleanly and without burrs on the inside. Cut a piece of $\frac{3}{16}$-inch tubing 4 inches long, or purchase a repair sleeve. Clean the capillary tube for a couple of inches back from each cut. Place the sleeve over the capillary ends so that it extends for at least $1\frac{1}{2}$ inches beyond the cuts. Solder the sleeve to the capillary at both ends with silver solder.

A search for leaks should include the motor terminals, where a leak will be evident by the presence of oil in addition to the formation of bubbles. You will be able to see the oil or pick it up with a finger. To stop a leak, tighten the terminal stud.

Once a leak has been found and repaired, it is sound practice to install a new drier-filter before further work is done. There is no way of telling whether the old drier-filter has lost its effectiveness—that is, whether some contamination and water vapor remained in the system after all repairs have been completed. A new drier-filter (Figure 55) is relatively inexpensive, easy to install, and helps guarantee a successful repair.

The drier-filter (sometimes called a molecular sieve) is often omitted on cheaper machines under the assumption that the sealed system contains factory materials free of impurities. This is a bad practice, since contaminants, particularly water vapor, can find their way into the system and cause constrictions, which in turn lead to unsatisfactory performance. Whenever a refrigerant system is worked on, even if the unit did not have a drier-filter to begin with, one should be installed.

New drier-filters are available with an attached purging valve, but these are more expensive than the type pictured, and are unnecessary.

To install a new drier-filter, remove a length of tubing in the high-pressure line several inches from the outlet of the condenser. The length removed should be $\frac{3}{4}$ inch less than the length of the drier-filter. This is done with tubing cutters, a relatively inexpensive tool. To cut the tubing, place it between the cutting discs (Figure 56 shows two types of tubing cutters), tighten the handle, and rotate the cutter in complete circles while continuing to tighten as needed until the tubing is severed.

Clean the ends of the copper tubing until they are shiny. Clean the ends of the drier-filter. Slide the ends of the drier-filter over the ends of the tubing for a distance of about $\frac{3}{8}$ inch and braze with silver solder.

If the ends of the drier-filter are not large enough to fit over the tubing, cut the gap in the tubing to the same length as the drier-filter and use a $\frac{3}{8}$-inch sleeve of tubing for each of the two connections.

After the leak has been found and repaired and the new drier-filter installed, the unit is sealed and the air trapped inside must be removed. This is done through a procedure called *purging* or *evacuating*. In commercial establishments a vacuum pump is used to purge a unit, but for home repair purposes the motor-compressor of the unit can do the job just as well.

The system must also be refilled

with the proper amount of Freon 12, a procedure called *charging*. Since charging immediately follows purging, preparations for both procedures are done simultaneously. Following are the tools and materials that will be needed and the manner in which they are used.

Figure 57 shows a disassembled *line tap valve,* with its "control" on the right. It is a means of regulated entrance to the sealed refrigerant system. Two line tap valves will be needed, one for purging and one for charging. Although the two are identical, to avoid confusion I will refer to each by its function, the *purging valve* and the *charging valve.*

The halves of the valve are separated by removing a Phillips screw on each side. The halves of the purging valve are then placed around the $\frac{1}{4}$-inch tubing a foot or so from the inlet to the motor-compressor, and the screws refastened.

Figure 58 shows the purging valve (less the control) installed on the suction line. The *needle screw,* the conical piece with a neoprene washer and a sharp point at its end, is now threaded loosely into the center of the assembly.

FIGURE 56

FIGURE 57

FIGURE 58

FIGURE 59

FIGURE 60

The *control* pictured in Figure 59 is used in conjunction with the purging valve. It consists of a threaded outlet (port), a fitting for connecting it to the purging valve, and a handle for opening and closing the needle screw.

At the end opposite the handle is a screwdriver bit. Place the bit into the slot on the head of the needle screw, then press down and attach the control to the purging valve by its threaded fitting. Hand tightening is sufficient.

Turn the control valve handle clockwise as far as it will go. This causes the needle screw to pierce the tubing and make a tight connection against it.

You are now ready to purge the system. Turn the control handle counterclockwise for a few turns in order to retract the point of the needle screw from the tubing and permit the exit of air from the otherwise sealed system. The purging valve remains open until purging has been completed. The control handle is then turned clockwise till hand tight. This is all the purging valve does: it punches a hole in the tubing to permit the trapped air in the system to leave, and then reseals the system.

In commercial work, the valve is omitted and the tubing is punctured with an awl. After evacuation, the hole is brazed shut. If you are confident of your ability to braze, you too can omit the purging valve, but I would recommend its use since it is cheap, sure, and requires no heat. (Whenever heat is applied, the risk of contamination increases.)

Figure 60 shows the purging valve and control installed. The valve is left in the *open position*.

Install the second or charging valve similarly, six inches or so from the inlet to the compressor. Leave the charging valve in the *open position*.

The instrument pictured in Figure 61 is called a *compound gauge*. It is used to measure pressure in the system when pressure is greater than that of the atmosphere, and it does so in *pounds per square inch*. It can also measure a vacuum, when atmospheric pressure is greater than that in the system, and does so in *inches of mercury*. The zero position on the gauge represents atmospheric pressure.

Ordinarily, a *pressure gauge* is used in conjunction with the compound gauge in order to read the higher pressures on the high or outlet side of

FIGURE 61

FIGURE 62

the motor-compressor. But since all our work will occur on the low side, a pressure gauge is unnecessary.

The hoses used with the compound gauge have a female fitting (with interior threads) at each end similar to those found on an ordinary garden house. Hand tighten one of the hoses between one of the two ports of the gauge and the charging valve. Turn the handle on the gauge clockwise and leave it *closed*.

Figure 62 shows a commercial cylinder of Freon 12. It contains 20 pounds of Freon when fully charged. Cans of Freon weighing about 1 pound are also available, and these are more than enough to charge a refrigerator. The proper amount of Freon to use in any particular unit is stated on the nameplate.

Freon, although harmless, is held in the container under high pressure, and precautions should be observed when handling it. These precautions are stated on the can.

Place the can of Freon on a kitchen scale before charging and note its weight. Stop charging when the weight of the can shows that the proper amount of Freon has been put into the system.

The Freon can comes equipped with a valve, and this valve is left closed through the evacuation procedure.

At this point, the purging valve and charging valve should be open, the gas and gauge valves closed. Hoses run from the Freon can and charging valve to the gauge. The system is ready to be purged and charged. Start the refrigerator.

If you now touch the purging valve, you can feel air being pumped out of the system. The needle on the gauge begins to fluctuate and will stabilize after a brief period. When the needle on the gauge reaches 2 or 3 inches of mercury (representing a partial vacuum) and remains stable for a couple of minutes, all the air in the system will have been evacuated (and your finger will no longer feel air being purged). With the refrigerator still running, close the purging valve by hand-tightening it in a clockwise direction.

Before charging can begin, the air now trapped in the hoses must be removed. Close the charging valve and open the valve on the can of Freon. Partially unscrew the hose at the gauge until whitish Freon shoots out of the connection, then retighten quickly. What you have done is use the high-pressure Freon to push air out of the hose, while simultaneously filling the hose with Freon. A similar procedure follows for the other hose: close the valve on the can of Freon and open the valve on the gauge; loosen the hose fitting slightly on the charging valve and tighten as soon as Freon shoots out; close the valve on the gauge and open the charging valve. The system is now ready to be charged. Note the weight of the can and deduct the weight needed for the charge to determine what the figure on the scale should be reached to complete charging.

The admittance of Freon into the closed system will be controlled by the gauge readings. It is essential that the release of gas into the system be done gradually and in short bursts so that the pressure never exceeds 15 pounds, and preferably stays below 9 pounds. Excessive pressure from the release of large amounts of Freon will push oil out of the sump of the motor-compressor and contaminate the system.

Open the gauge valve for a second or so, then shut it. Keep watching the gauge. The needle should not be allowed to go above 9 pounds. Allow the motor-compressor to pump the just-admitted Freon through the system

for a while, wait until the gauge pressure drops slightly, then reopen the gauge valve and admit more. As the amount of Freon in the system increases, the settled gauge readings will move upward and the upper portion of the condenser will begin to feel warm. Keep adding gas in short bursts until all of the required amount is in the system.

Typical operating pressure on the low side (the one we are monitoring) is between 3 and 5 pounds per square inch. This will vary with different machines, but if the variance is great, the proper amount of gas has not been used. For example, if the gauge reads 2 pounds of pressure after the supposedly correct amount of Freon has been introduced and allowed to circulate for several minutes, it is quite possible that the scale used to weigh the Freon is not accurate; this would be confirmed by the fact that the condenser still feels close to room temperature. If the pressure is significantly greater, if too much gas has been introduced, frost will appear on the condenser lines. So it always helps to know what the low-side pressure should be on the particular unit involved, as well as the weight of Freon required.

If one remains doubtful about the amount of gas that has been put into the system after the unit has been allowed to run for at least ten minutes, an alternate check should be made with the amprobe. Compare the amprobe reading with the normal running amperage draw stated on the nameplate. If it is higher, with frost present on the return tubing, open the purging valve slightly and allow Freon to escape until the amperage is reduced to normal. Conversely, if the reading is lower than normal and there is other evidence that not enough gas has been introduced (such as a cool condenser), continue charging the system until the amperage draw is up to normal.

After the proper amount of Freon is in the system, close the charging valve, remove the control attachment, and screw on the valve cap. (Make sure the washer is in the cap.) Remove the control from the purging valve and cap it. Shut off the valve on the can of Freon. Uncouple the hoses, and charging is complete.

SITUATION I:
At times ice cubes are melting, at times frozen solid. Unit is running far more than usual. Door gasket and

FIGURE 63

light bulb are all right. Food isn't crammed into cabinet, condenser is clean, thermostat is functioning properly. There is no oil on floor, no symptoms of a leak. The behavior of the machine is erratic and unsatisfactory.

This malfunction is most likely a restriction in the refrigerant system, some foreign material such as water which has frozen. Its usual location is near the ends of the capillary tube, more rarely further inside the tubing. The position of ice inside the capillary is visible as frost on the outside. Turn on the refrigerator and place a lighted match under the frosted area. If ice is causing the blockage, the frost will disappear and gurgling sounds will be heard as the Freon flows freely again.

Allow the unit to keep running and return to the spot an hour or so later. If no frost has built up, the problem was temporary and has been solved. If after a longer period of usage, the only solution is to shut off the unit, cut out the section of capillary which contains the blockage, and replace it with a new section. The procedure has been described previously (page 40). Along with the repair, a new

drier-filter should be added, and the system purged and recharged.

SITUATION J:

1. Amprobe reading shows an amperage draw significantly higher than normal.

2. There is oil on the floor and it contains amber flecks.

3. Motor will not start using direct-start cord (see page 11).

4. Multitester shows there is no continuity between terminal C and S, C and R, or both.

5. Test lamp will not light on either C and S terminals, C and R terminals, or both.

Any of the above symptoms evidences a faulty or inoperative motor-compressor. Before replacing a motor-compressor, it is best to weigh a number of considerations.

Since the motor-compressor is a sealed unit and cannot be repaired at home, a replacement must be purchased. The replacement may cost anywhere from $50 to $80, and possibly more. Rarely will it be less. In addition to the expense of charging tools and materials, one is likely to incur the cost of cleaning the entire system in order to remove contaminants. This requires a 50–50 mixture of Freon 11 and nitrogen, injected into the system at high pressure. With home refrigeration repairs only now beginning to become widespread, both Freon 11 and nitrogen must still be purchased in bulk, adding greatly to the expense of the individual refrigerator owner contemplating the replacement of a motor-compressor. The total cost involved could well be more than the unit is worth.

Refrigerators with perfectly good motor-compressors are scrapped every day in large numbers. They can often be obtained for a very nominal price, even for nothing, if they are picked up from the junk dealer. The motor-compressor should of course be tested first with the direct-start cord and amprobe. If it checks out all right and is suitable for your unit, replacement of the motor-compressor becomes economically worthwhile.

To remove and replace a motor-compressor:

1. Remove the three leads to the motor terminals.

2. Use the cut-off and pinching tool pictured in Figure 63 to cut and seal the inlet and outlet tubing to the motor-compressor a few inches from the two connections.

3. Remove the four bolts that hold the motor-compressor to its metal frame.

4. Mount the replacement motor-compressor to the frame with the four bolts.

5. Use a tubing cutter to remove the pinched ends, then reconnect the ends with $\frac{5}{16}$-inch diameter sleeves and silver solder.

6. Reattach each motor lead to the terminal from which it was disconnected.

7. Evacuate the system and recharge with Freon 12 as previously described (see pages 41–45).

3

ROOM AIR CONDITIONERS

Figures 64 and 65 show a Westinghouse room air conditioner with and without its cover (the cover lifts off after the screws along its perimeter are removed). It uses 220 volts and is rated at 12,000 Btu (British thermal units), or one ton of refrigeration. This is the amount of heat the unit will remove per hour. Although procedures in this chapter refer to this particular unit, they are applicable to all makes and models of air conditioners.

The sealed *refrigerant system* of an air conditioner is essentially the same as that of a refrigerator. The specific means of correcting malfunctions in the sealed refrigerant system of the air conditioner will be found in the later sections of the previous chapter.

Figure 66 is a side view of the unit.

On the right of the photo, at the front of the machine directly behind the grille that faces the room, is the *evaporator*. It is here that heat is removed from the room air through the system's refrigerant, Freon 22. On the left of the photo, at the outdoor-facing back of the machine, is the *condenser*. This is the component of the sealed system which removes the heat absorbed from the room air as well as the heat created when the Freon is compressed. These two components are separated by a partition called a *bulkhead*.

The condenser has a protective grille on the outside, detachable by removing eight screws along its perimeter. Figure 67 shows the back of the unit with this grille removed.

The evaporator also has a grille which is removed by lifting and pulling it away from the machine. Pictured in Figure 68 is the evaporator with the grille removed. A *filter pad,* used to screen out dirt in the air coming in from outside, is attached to the back of the front grille.

On the lower-left control panel are three knobs. The one on the left controls the position of a *vent* at the bulkhead, so that room air may be exhausted, or fresh air drawn in from outside, or the air in the room circulated. It is a mechanical control; the door or flap of the vent is shifted to any of its three positions by means of an attached cable.

The second knob is attached to a *selector switch* that has five positions:

FIGURE 64

FIGURE 66

FIGURE 65

FIGURE 67

FIGURE 68

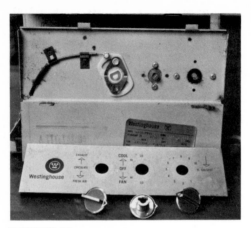

FIGURE 69

OFF, LOW FAN, HIGH FAN, LOW COOL, and HIGH COOL. The two "cool" positions activate both the refrigerant system and the two fans; the two "fan" positions activate only the fans.

Both fans are driven by a single fan motor; they are attached to opposite ends of its shaft. The evaporator fan is the "squirrel cage" type and is on the room side of the bulkhead. The condenser fan is a blade type and is located on the outdoor side of the bulkhead, visible in Figure 67.

The third knob is attached to a *thermostat*. It is numbered from one to ten; the higher the number, the cooler the room will be when the unit is operating normally.

SITUATION A:
The air conditioner is running but the room isn't being cooled at all. The thermostat is set at one of its normal "on" positions. The selector switch is on HIGH COOL. No air is being blown through the grille. *The grille feels cold.*

The key symptom is the cold grille. This indicates that electricity is being delivered to the unit and the refrigerant system is working. Were it not, no cooling would be obtained and the grille would be at room temperature. The fact that no air is being blown shows that the fan blades aren't turning. Conceivably, both fans could be loose on the motor shaft, but it is far more likely that the fan motor is not running.

The failure of a fan motor may be due to a defective selector switch (rarely), a defective fan motor (occasionally), or a *faulty starting capacitor* (one of the two most common malfunctions in air conditioners).

The fan capacitor is an electrical component that helps start the motor by providing a brief but powerful electrical charge. Its time of operation is no more than a few seconds.

To get at the capacitor for testing, unplug the machine, press down on the front grille and pull it out. Place your hand against the evaporator. It will probably be cold and may even have ice on it.

With the grille removed, two screws at the top of the control panel become visible. Remove both. The panel, hinged at the bottom, can now be swung down to provide access to the components behind it, as shown in Figure 69.

Two electrical components at the bulkhead are now visible (see Figure 70). The larger of the two is an electrical relay, the smaller is the fan starting capacitor. DO NOT TOUCH THE CAPACITOR TERMINALS. The capacitor stores a potent electrical charge, which must be dissipated before handling.

To remove the charge, take hold of the rubber-sheathed handle of an insulated screwdriver and place the blade across the two terminals as pictured in Figure 71. (For clarity, the capacitor has been moved out for the photograph, but it's best to dissipate the charge before moving it.)

After the charge has been dissipated, remove the screw from the curved metal strap that holds both components to the bulkhead. Color-code the wires and two terminals for reattachment and remove the two leads to the capacitor. Remove the capacitor.

A defective capacitor will often show deformation caused by internal swelling. Another symptom is "bleeding," liquid seepage along its exterior seams. In either case, the capacitor is defective and should be replaced.

If neither condition is present, attach the two main alligator clips of the direct-start cord to the capacitor terminals, plug in the cord to a wall outlet momentarily, then remove the

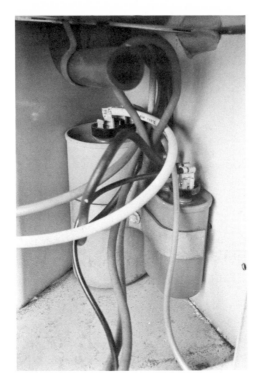

FIGURE 70

FIGURE 71

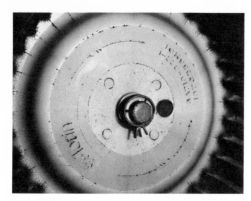

FIGURE 72

plug. Place the blade of the insulated screwdriver across the capacitor terminals and listen for a clicking sound. If you hear it, the capacitor is all right. If no click is heard, the capacitor is faulty.

The capacitor may also be checked with the multitester. Place the selector switch at the RX 1000 position and touch the capacitor terminals with the probes. If the needle deflects and comes to rest at zero or slightly below, there is a short in the capacitor and it is defective. If the needle doesn't deflect but remains on the infinity sign, the capacitor is "open" and is also defective. If the needle deflects and provides a reading of 100,000 or above, the capacitor is all right.

Capacitors are rated by mfd (*microfarads,* a unit of capacitance and voltage). When obtaining a replacement capacitor, it it preferable though not necessary to buy an exact duplicate of the defective one. It *is* essential that the new capacitor have the same ratings as the one being replaced. And remember that while a 220-volt capacitor will work on a 110-volt circuit, the reverse does not hold true.

Install the new capacitor by reversing the procedure used to get at and remove the old one.

If the capacitor in the machine tests out as operational, prepare the multitester for testing continuity in the fan motor.

The fan motor is located on the outdoor side of the bulkhead. While the terminals of the motor-compressor emerge from the motor-compressing housing, the leads of the fan motor are connected inside the fan motor housing. They come into the room side through a hole in the bulkhead directly above and behind the capacitor—one lead is colored brown and the other black—and are attached to the capacitor. Two other wires, colored yellow and red, are attached to the selector switch mounted on the back of the control panel.

To test the fan motor for continuity, remove the yellow wire from the switch prong, and place one probe on the terminal connector and the other on the red-wire terminal. If the needle deflects and comes to rest around 6 ohms, the running-winding phase of the fan motor has continuity and is functional. To test the starting-winding phase, place one probe on the yellow-wire terminal connector and the other on the brown-wire terminal of the capacitor. If the needle deflects and comes to rest at about 10 ohms, the starting-winding phase is functional.

Both tests must evidence continuity or the motor is defective.

If both tests show continuity, your next step is to test for grounding. Scrape a bit of paint off the motor housing so that bare metal shows. Place one probe on the bare metal and the other alternately on the three wire terminal connectors—red, brown, and black. *If any of these three tests shows continuity, the motor is grounded and must be replaced.*

To remove the defective motor, first detach the motor leads, then remove the wire mesh and insulation from in front of the evaporator fan.

Figure 72 shows the "squirrel-cage" evaporator fan. In some units it is held to the motor shaft by a set screw through its hub, or by a thin steel strip that lies in a milled slot in the shaft and hub. It may even be held by a combination of a "key" and set screw (the key is a small piece of steel that fits into a groove milled in the shaft and hub). Whatever the means of attachment, the evaporator fan must be taken off the shaft before the motor can be removed.

The motor and condenser-fan blade are positioned on the outdoor side of the bulkhead. The motor is attached to the bulkhead by screws or bolts. Remove the screws or bolts, and the motor with the attached condenser fan can be lifted out.

As can be seen in Figure 73, the condenser-fan blade is attached to the motor shaft by a flat piece of steel wedged into a slot in the shaft. Remove this piece and pull off the condenser-fan blade. A replacement motor is installed by reversing the procedure for removing the defective one.

In the unlikely event that both the capacitor and motor are found functional, a continuity check of the selector switch should be made, either with the multitester or a buzzer tester.

To test for continuity with the buzzer, trace the wiring from the appliance cord and attach an alligator clip to the terminal connector that runs the hot incoming wire to the switch. Number the outgoing terminals: 1, 2, 3, 4. Attach the other alligator clip to terminal 1. With the switch in the OFF position, no buzzing should be heard. Rotate the selector switch through the four "on" positions and listen to buzzing as evidence of continuity. When buzzing is heard,

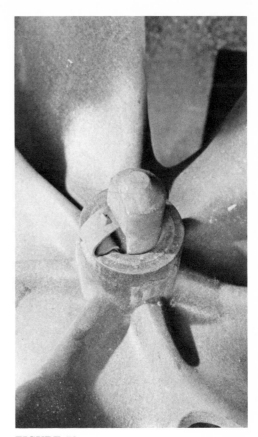

FIGURE 73

FIGURE 74

shift the alligator clip from terminal 1 to terminal 2 and test again through the "on" positions. When buzzing is heard, repeat the test on terminal 3, then terminal 4. On each test, buzzing must occur or continuity has been lost and the switch is defective.

To replace a defective selector switch, pull off the knob, lift out the leads attached to the switch terminals, remove the two screws that fasten the switch to the control panel, and install a new selector switch by reversing the procedure.

SITUATION B:
The thermostat is set at any "on" position. You turn the selector switch to LOW COOL, HIGH COOL, LOW FAN, **or** HIGH FAN, **but hear no sounds of a running motor. No air is being circulated, no cooling is taking effect.**

When an air conditioner seems "dead," unless an extraordinary coincidence is involved, the cause of the malfunction is either an unplugged or defective appliance cord, a faulty selector switch, or trouble in the house wiring.

The procedure for testing house

wiring is detailed in Chapter 1 (pages 3–6) and should now be followed, since a blown fuse caused by inadequate house wiring is one of the most common causes of a "dead" air conditioner.

In most homes a separate outlet is provided for the refrigerator, but not for room air conditioners. The unit must be plugged into a wall outlet which usually has a capacity of only 15 amperes, with a number of other appliances or lights on the same circuit. Inevitably, the circuit overloads and its fuse blows.

The ordinary house wiring circuit has a maximum theoretical capacity of 15 amperes, but in practice the fuse will blow at about 12 or 13 amperes. An air conditioner rated at 4,000 or 5,000 Btu will ordinarily draw in the neighborhood of 6 amperes, and these are among the smallest manufactured. It is obvious that with half the capacity of the circuit being used by the unit, a few additional lights and another appliance or two will drain its capacity, and it will be exhausted.

There is no permanent solution to this situation except to install a new and adequate electrical line to the unit. A temporary expedient is to replace the burned fuse and keep lights and other appliances off the same circuit while the unit is in use.

If inadequate house wiring has not caused the malfunction, the appliance cord should be tested. To gain access to the wire ends inside the machine, remove the front grille and the two screws that attach the control panel to the frame of the unit (Figure 74). The panel is hinged at its bottom and can now be swung down.

The selector switch is the center knob, with positions for HIGH FAN, LOW COOL, and so forth. Unplug the unit and prepare the multitester.

The appliance cord (pictured at the bottom of Figure 75) has three wires under its protective outer insulation. Each of these wires is separated from the others by an additional covering of insulation. With the control panel down, it will be seen that one of these wires, usually covered green, leaves the appliance cord and is connected to a screw fastened to the frame (Figure 76). This is the grounding wire; at its opposite end is the round prong on the plug. Its purpose is to protect the user against accidental shocks; a safety device, it is not a part of the 220-volt system.

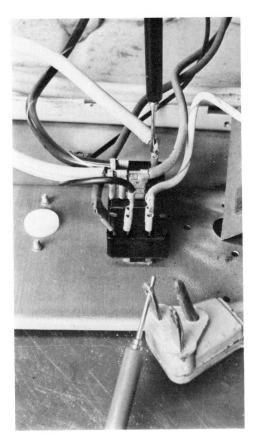

FIGURE 75

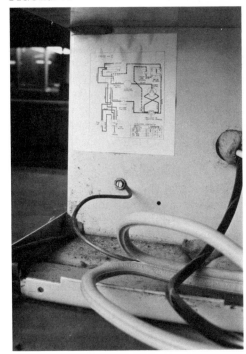

FIGURE 76

Find the ends of the other two wires. Bring the plug to within a foot or so of these control-panel ends. Place one probe on a *flat* prong of the plug and the other on either of the two wire ends. If no continuity is obtained, shift the probe on the flat prong to the other flat prong (there are two wires to be tested and the probes may be on different wires). If no continuity is evidenced, the appliance cord is defective.

If continuity is obtained in either test, change the position of both probes, to the other flat prong and to the second wire end. If no continuity is obtained, the appliance cord is defective. *Both* wires must evidence continuity or the appliance cord is defective.

To replace a defective cord, remove its leads from the control panel and detach the screw that holds the grounding wire. In replacing a defective cord, it is essential that the grounding wire be attached to the frame as pictured in Figure 76.

If the house wiring and appliance cord have both been found operational, the selector switch should be tested next. This procedure has been described in the previous section, as

has the replacement of a defective selector switch.

SITUATION C:

You turn the selector switch to LOW COOL or HIGH COOL. Air begins to blow, but even after the unit has been running for ten minutes or so, it doesn't feel cool. You listen carefully but cannot hear the motor-compressor running. The grille remains at room temperature and the room itself isn't being cooled.

The fact that air is being blown into the room is evidence that the motor fan is working and electricity is being delivered to the unit. The fact that this air is not being cooled indicates an inoperative motor-compressor. When a motor-compressor fails to operate, the cause is more frequently to be found in a malfunctioning electrical component than in the motor-compressor itself, so these components should be tested first.

Swing the control panel face down and test the selector switch for continuity, as previously described. If the switch evidences a lack of continuity, replace it and your problem is solved. But the failure of a selector switch is

rare, and in the situation we are dealing with, the operating fans would indicate at least some continuity in the switch.

If the switch evidences continuity, as it probably will, the next component to check is the thermostat, which is located next to the switch and has a knob with which to select greater or less cooling.

Any of three types of thermostat is used in room air conditioners: the bulb, capillary, or bimetal types shown in Figure 77.

In the *bulb* and *capillary* types, a volatile liquid vaporizes as the temperature rises and, at a preset level, creates enough pressure in the thermostat to bring its contacts together and close the circuit to the motor-compressor, enabling it to run. As the temperature then falls, the vapor is condensed back to a liquid, the pressure in the thermostat switch decreases, and its contacts open to interrupt the flow of electricity to the motor-compressor.

In the *bimetal* thermostat, a strip composed of two different metals arcs away from a stationary contact when the temperature rises above a preset level, thereby opening the circuit to the motor-compressor. Conversely, as the temperature falls, the bimetal strip straightens, makes contact with the stationary contact, and closes the circuit to the motor-refrigerator. Thermostats may fail in any open position because of a lost charge in the sensory alarm, and in a closed position due to welded contacts or misalignment of internal linkages.

The capillary or bulb thermostat should be tested between 70° and 80°F, for these are the temperatures at which their contacts will come together and separate. If the thermostat is colder than 70°F, warm it in your hand. If the thermostat is warmer than 80°F, place it (bulb or capillary only) in cold water. You should be able to hear the on and off clicks, though for some thermostats the sound will be quite faint.

To check the thermostat for continuity, place the probes of the multitester on its terminals. The meter will read infinite resistance when the contacts are open and show continuity when the contacts are closed. Both tests must check out if the thermostat is functional.

To remove a defective thermostat of the bimetal type (as in this unit), pull

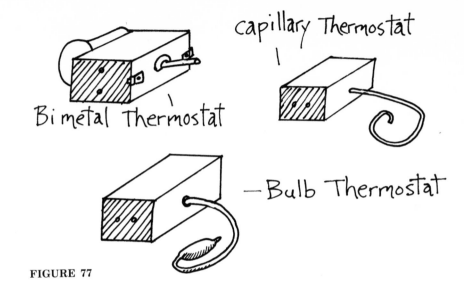

FIGURE 77

off the knob, remove the leads and the two screws that attach the thermostat to the back of the control panel, and the thermostat is free. Install the replacement by reversing the procedure, taking particular care to place the new thermostat in the same position as the old one.

If the thermostat is of the capillary feeler or bulb type, even greater care must be taken to place the new feeler or bulb in the same position as the old one. Figure 78 shows the thermostat attached to the evaporator and Figure 79 shows it attached to the side of the blower. A bulb mounted on the evaporator must be wrapped in insulation. The bare bulb or capillary *must not* touch the evaporator. If it does, the bulb will be reading temperatures colder than the air stream and will shut off electricity to the motor-compressor before the desired cooling is obtained. (Conversely, if the bulb is too far from the evaporator it will be sensing too warm a

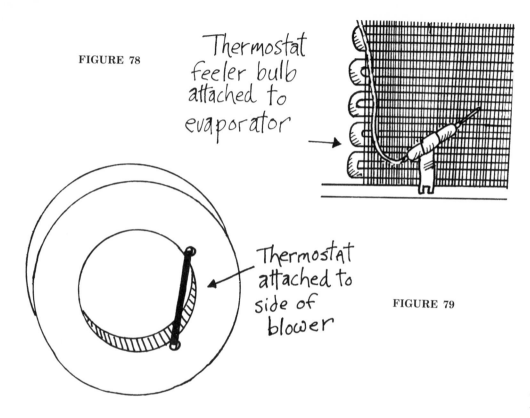

FIGURE 78

Thermostat feeler bulb attached to evaporator

Thermostat attached to side of blower

FIGURE 79

temperature and the unit will run excessively.)

Complete failure of a thermostat, with no cooling effect at all, is rare. More usually, a thermostat becomes defective just to the point of causing erratic cooling.

If the switch and thermostat both work, the next component to check is the *relay*. The relay (Figure 80) is located beside the fan capacitor on the room side of the bulkhead. (Its more precise location varies in different units.) A defective relay is a

common cause of an inoperative motor-compressor.

Relays become defective when their contacts are fused together, or burn and do not make contact, or when the pickup coil shorts out and opens.

To test the relay, disconnect the appliance cord and all external wires to the relay. Refer to the unit's wiring diagram to determine which terminals represent the pickup coil and which the contacts.

Prepare the multitester and place its probe on each of the three pickup terminals. If no continuity is evidenced, replace the relay. If continuity is evidenced, further tests are in order.

Place the probes on the contact terminals. The contacts of a relay are normally open, so *if continuity is registered, the relay is defective.* If continuity is not registered, manually close the relay contacts and replace the probes on the contact terminals. This time, if continuity is *not* registered, the relay is defective.

All three tests must be made to determine whether the relay is defective.

The relay contacts should also be inspected closely. If burned, they may be cleaned with a file to restore operability. If they are welded shut, the relay must be replaced.

To replace a defective relay, remove the strap which holds it (and the capacitor; be sure to dissipate charge of the capacitor as on page 51) to the bulkhead by removing the single screw through the strap and bulkhead. Detach the leads to the relay. Install the replacement by reversing the procedure.

If the switch, thermostat, and relay all prove functional, it will be necessary to remove the unit's housing in order to get at the remaining electrical components. The cover is attached by screws along its perimeter and can be lifted off when these are removed.

With the unit's housing removed, the motor-compressor becomes accessible. The protective cover pictured in Figure 81 sits on top of the motor-compressor case and covers the motor terminals. Ordinarily the overload, a protective electrical component to be tested, will be found under the same cover, or nearby. The cover is held by a metal strap and is removed by pulling up one end of the strap. The cover will then lift off.

On the right of Figure 82 is the small electrical device called an *over-*

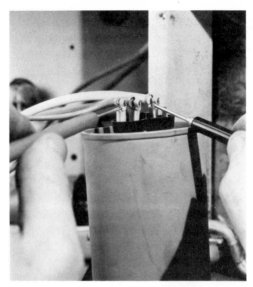

FIGURE 80

FIGURE 81

FIGURE 82

FIGURE 83

load (guardette). When the motor draws excessive current, it creates heat which in turn opens the contacts in the overload. Since electricity to the motor must pass through the overload first, continuity is lost and the motor will shut off. The contacts in the overload will remain open for several minutes until the heat dissipates and will then return to their normal closed position, at which point continuity is reestablished and the motor restarts.

To test the overload, remove the appliance cord from the outlet and prepare the multitester for continuity testing. The overload terminals are normally closed, so at least two minutes should be allowed for the overload to cool before testing. Place a probe on each of the overload terminals (see Figure 83). If no continuity is observed on the ohm scale, the overload is defective.

To replace a defective overload, detach the leads to its terminals, lift it out of the motor terminal box, and install the replacement overload by reversing the procedure.

Overloads rarely become defective unless another electrical component such as the capacitor (starting or running) becomes defective first and

causes the overload to cycle the
motor on and off too frequently. It is
therefore prudent to check for other
malfunctioning electrical components if the overload is found to be
defective.

If all of these tests have found all
components to be functional, the
motor itself must be checked. The
simplest way to do this is through a
direct-start cord. (The way to make a
direct-start cord is detailed in the
first chapter, page 11.)

Disconnect the appliance cord and
all leads to the motor terminals.
There are three terminals: one
marked C for Common, one S for
Start, and one R for Run. Attach the
alligator clips of the direct-start cord
to the three terminals, plug in the
cord, and turn the switch on for a
couple of seconds but *no longer.* If the
motor runs, the cause of the malfunction lies elsewhere. If it doesn't run,
the motor is defective and must be replaced.

An alternative method of testing
the motor is to place the probes of the
multitester on the terminals C and S
(see Figure 84). If the needle on the
scale comes to rest at about 20 ohms,
the starting mechanism is functional.
If there is no deflection, the motor has

FIGURE 84

lost continuity in the starting mechanism and is defective.

If the starting mechanism shows continuity, leave the one probe on the C terminal and shift the other from the S to the R terminal. If continuity is evidenced, the motor is functional. If no continuity is evidenced, the motor is defective.

If continuity is found in both the start and run positions, scrape away a bit of paint on the motor case with a knife so that bare metal is exposed. Place one probe on the C terminal and the other on the bare metal. If continuity is evidenced, the motor is grounded and must be replaced. If no continuity is evidenced, repeat the grounding test with one probe on the S and then the R terminal, and the other probe on bare metal. If any of these three tests shows continuity, the motor is defective.

When the motor-compressor is found to be defective, the choice of whether to replace it or scrap the entire unit should be weighed. Some manufacturers give a five-year warranty on the motor-compressor, and if this is still in effect, it should, of course, be utilized. If the warranty is no longer in effect, the cost of a new motor-compressor is likely to be at

least $60. It will rarely be less and frequently a lot more. Since the motor-compressor is part of the sealed system, replacing it will also entail the cost of the tools and materials required for purging and recharging the system. The total expense will be a minimum of $100, and likely more. If the unit is rated at 6,000 Btu or less, replacing it with a new air conditioner of the same capacity will be less than $200. Unless you intend to do refrigeration repairs involving more than the one air conditioner, I would suggest getting a repair estimate from a commercial establishment. It is possible, in this particular instance, that their estimate will be lower than your cost. (This is the only case where home repair is unlikely to be advantageous.)

If the unit is rated at more than 6,000 Btu, it will probably be more economical to replace the defective motor yourself, a procedure detailed at the end of the previous chapter.

SITUATION D:
You switch on the machine to HIGH COOL. Cool air begins to blow but after a while you notice that the room is warmer than you'd expected it to be by now, although the unit has been running continuously. You turn the thermostat to 10. The unit continues to run but the room does not become appreciably cooler. The air being blown feels somewhat cooler than the air in the room, but not markedly so.

A wide variety of malfunctions can cause this condition. They can be divided into malfunctions of the unit itself, and malfunctions external to it. Among the latter, one of the most common is a dirty filter.

Figure 85 shows a typical filter, located on the back of the front grille. It is a spongelike pad designed to permit the passage of air while trapping dirt, dust, and other foreign matter. If the dirt it traps is allowed to accumulate, the passage of air will become restricted to a point that results in unsatisfactory cooling.

Some manufacturers recommend that the filter be cleaned every thirty days, others suggest every seven days of running time. Neither recommendation may fit your own situation, since a filter clogs faster in areas where there is more dust in the air circulated by the air conditioner. Cleaning the filter every three days of running time is a good practice in mid-Manhattan, but thirty days of running time will not clog the filter if it is circulating in the Sierras. It is best to clean the filter more often than seems needed at first, and then if there is no evidence of clogging, to reduce the frequency until the proper equation for your area is found.

The filter is cleaned by vacuuming, then washing in warm water and wringing dry.

Another common cause of unsatisfactory cooling is a dirty condenser. This is the component in which the hot Freon 22 refrigerant is cooled and returned to its liquid state. If the condenser is matted with dirt (and being on the outdoor side of the bulkhead, it is susceptible to dirt accumulation), the heat which the Freon has absorbed during compression and in the evaporator will have difficulty passing from the condenser to the cooler surrounding air, and the result will be a marked impairment of cooling capacity. The condenser should be cleaned at least once a year—by vacuuming, scrubbing with a wire brush, then vacuuming again, and finally wiping with a damp rag.

The hot air being exhausted from the condenser area must be free to discharge itself into the atmosphere. Any blockage (such as a winter cover)

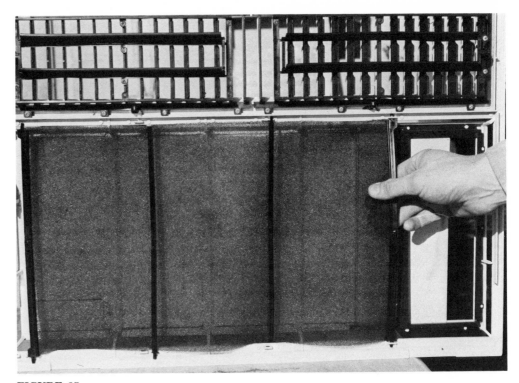

FIGURE 85

FIGURE 86

which brings the hot air back toward the unit or prevents its free flow outward will result in unsatisfactory cooling.

Another possible cause of unsatisfactory cooling is the incorrect positioning of the vent, particularly on hot and humid days. Figure 86 shows the three positions of the vent. If the vent is on EXHAUST or FRESH AIR, the unit is probably doing its best and is simply too small to handle hot and humid fresh air, or relatively warmer air from other rooms. The vent should be shut so that only the already-cooled air in the room is recirculated. This should reduce the room's temperature.

If the vent is shut and the resulting drop in temperature is still insufficient, a temperature comparison of the air entering and leaving the unit on the room side will determine whether something is wrong with the cooling system or whether the room being cooled is simply too large for the unit to service adequately. Two dry-bulb thermometers and a bit of permagum are necessary. Affix the thermometers to the front grille with dabs of permagum, positioning one in the incoming and one in the outgoing air flow. The bulbs should

not touch the grille. Allow several minutes before reading the temperatures. A unit that is functioning normally will usually show a temperature difference of about 20°F. On a very hot and humid day the difference will be less, but anything less than a 10°F difference indicates either a faulty refrigerant system or a unit too small for the job.

Very often people buy small units because they know that their house wiring is inadequate. They choose a unit that draws a relatively low amperage, rather than one that will meet their cooling requirements.

The unit-selection chart on page 66 is a *guide* for selecting the proper air conditioner. If the room to be cooled has a southern or western exposure, large unshaded windows, an uninsulated roof, or large openings to unconditioned areas, or if you expect to be moving in and out of the room frequently, the unit should be greater than the chart indicates. Conversely, factors such as a northern exposure, full shade, and so forth, would permit a smaller unit than is given. The chart is an average of residential needs and should be approached as a general guide, then modified for a particular room.

An air conditioner with too large a capacity for the room it is to cool is also unsatisfactory. The function of the unit is to create a comfortable climate in the room, and one aspect of this is the removal of humidity from the air. When the unit is too large, it lowers the temperature too quickly and shuts off the motor-compressor before the air can be adequately dehumidified. The result is needless discomfort.

Too high or too low voltage will also result in unsatisfactory cooling. To determine the voltage, prepare the multitester and place the selector knob at the 250 AC position. Insert the probes into the slots of the outlet from which the unit is receiving electricity and read the voltage on the red AC scale.

If the unit is rated for 115 volts, the minimum necessary voltage for proper operation is 103 and the maximum 126. If the unit is rated at 208 volts, the minimum is 187 and the maximum 228. The voltage ratings of the unit will be on its nameplate.

If the unit is operating on voltages beyond the limits given, it will not provide satisfactory cooling. The problem lies either in the house wiring or the utility power source.

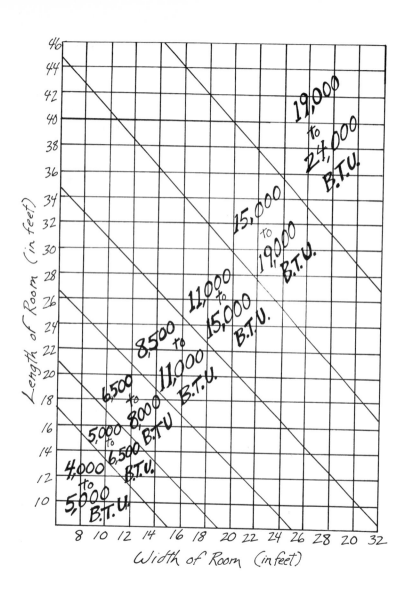

Length of Room (in feet)

Width of Room (in feet)

Another common cause of unsatisfactory cooling is the placement of furniture in the path of the unit's air flow. In addition to blocking the distribution of cold air around the room, the movement of air by convection is markedly reduced, which in turn creates pockets of colder and warmer air and contributes to a feeling of discomfort.

Unsatisfactory cooling caused by malfunctions of the refrigerant system is much less frequent than that caused by external factors, but such malfunctions do occur. They are treated in the same way as malfunctions in the refrigerant system of a refrigerator, and the ways to correct them are detailed in the sealed-system section of the previous chapter (pages 32–45).

A common malfunction of an air conditioner's sealed system is the partial loss of Freon 22 due to a leak. If the leak is tiny, as it often is, the unit will continue to function but its ability to cool the room will gradually decrease. When this occurs, a reading with the amprobe should be taken. If there has been a loss of Freon, the reading on the amprobe will be lower than the figure given on the nameplate. (It is important to remember that the figure on the nameplate is the amperage draw under *normal* running conditions, neither the maximum nor minimum encountered under varying operating conditions.)

The partial loss of refrigerant can also be confirmed by feeling the evaporator coils. The coil closest to the evaporator entrance will be coldest, and indeed will feel normal, but each other coil will feel warmer the further its position from the evaporator entrance.

To correct this malfunction, the leak must first be found and plugged. A new drier-filter is then installed, and finally the sealed system is purged and recharged. All these procedures are detailed in the refrigerant repair section of the previous chapter (pages 32–45).

Unsatisfactory cooling will also result if the motor-compressor begins to lose its effectiveness. This will be evidenced by a *higher* than normal draw when measured with the amprobe. For replacement of the motor-compressor, see pages 46–47.

A restriction in the capillary tube can also cause unsatisfactory cooling.

The capillary shown in Figure 87 is $\frac{1}{8}$ inch in diameter. Contaminants in the sealed system, including water

vapor, can easily restrict the capillary or block it completely. This will be evidenced by frost accumulation in the blocked area and erratic or unsatisfactory cooling, or none at all.

To correct the condition, first try warming the blocked area with a match in the hope that the blockage is caused by ice. If it is ice, it will melt and a gurgling will be heard as the area is unblocked. The water vapor will pass through the drier-filter and, one hopes, be removed.

If warming the blocked area does not clear the restriction, or if the restriction recurs, the capillary tube must be cut and the blocked section removed. A sleeve is then brazed into the removed area, a new drier-filter installed, and the system purged and recharged (see pages 38–45).

SITUATION E:
You turn on the air conditioner to HIGH COOL. Cold air blows for a few minutes, then the motor stops. It comes on again a few minutes later, runs for a while, and stops again. The sequence repeats, and all the while the room is not being cooled satisfactorily.

This condition can be caused by a thermostat feeler bulb touching the

FIGURE 87

evaporator, a dirty condenser, condenser air being blown back toward the unit, low voltage, or a faulty overload. Testing for each of these possible causes has been detailed in previous sections.

SITUATION F:

You switch the air conditioner to HIGH COOL or LOW COOL. The unit blows out cold air for a few minutes and stops. You can hear the motor-compressor running. The grille area remains cold, but no air is blown out. Several minutes later, cold air starts to blow again for a short while, then stops. This pattern continues and the room is hardly being cooled at all.

Whenever air stops blowing into the room, it can only mean that the evaporator fan (squirrel-cage type) has ceased to turn. The fact that it turns intermittently indicates that the overload inside the fan motor case is shutting off power to the motor. It may do so because of excessive heat, or because the overload itself has become defective.

To correct the condition, remove the cabinet cover and examine the fan motor for dirt. The fan motor lies on the outdoor side of the bulkhead and,

despite its protective cover, accumulates dirt, dust, and grime. When it labors against such fouling, excessive heat is created and the overload cuts off electricity to the motor.

If dirt does not appear to be the problem, turn the fan blades manually to see whether force is required. It should move freely with a flick of the finger. If it is binding, place a few drops of #10 oil in the motor oiling hole and spin the blade until the oil works through to the shaft and the binding ceases.

If neither dirt nor a binding fan shaft is the problem, either the overload is defective or the fan motor itself is behaving abnormally and causing the functional overload to open the circuit. It doesn't pay to investigate which of the two is at fault, since either a defective overload or a defective motor require that the motor be replaced.

Replacement of the fan motor has been detailed on page 53.

SITUATION G:

You switch on the machine and the fuse blows (or the breaker trips). You replace the fuse (or switch on the breaker) and the fuse blows (or breaker trips off) again.

This condition is most frequently caused by overloaded house wiring. A temporary expedient is to remove all lights and appliances on the same circuit as the air conditioner, but the only long-range solution is to install a new line for the unit.

If overloading the circuit is not the cause of the malfunction, the next most likely possibility is a faulty capacitor. The procedure for checking capacitors is detailed on pages 50–52.

If the capacitor is functional, test the relay as detailed on pages 58–59.

If both the capacitor and relay are functional and the fuse-blowing is not being caused by an overloaded circuit, still another possibility is a jammed compressor.

To test for this, unplug the unit and remove both the cabinet cover and the cover over the motor terminals. Remove all leads to the terminals.

Attach the alligator clips of the direct-start cord to the three terminals. Plug in the cord, turn on the switch, wait a couple of seconds at most, then turn it off. If the motor does not start to run freely, or starts and stops before the switch has been turned off, the motor-compressor is jammed and must be replaced.

If the motor-compressor starts and

runs freely, and the capacitor and relay have been tested and found to be functional, there are only two remaining possibilities. Both occur infrequently. The first is a wire that was broken and is touching metal and causing a short; the other is an erroneous connection in the wiring.

To check for a broken lead, first inspect the wires. If there is a tear in the insulation, a cut, or any sign of a possible break, place a probe on each end of the suspected wire. If no continuity is evidenced, even if the break is not visible, replace the wire. One has to be prepared to spend time when hunting down a broken wire that is causing a short and blowing fuses.

To check for incorrect wiring, first consult the unit's wiring diagram. Each wire is color-coded. By referring to the wiring diagram and noting the colors for each wire, every connection can be examined and its proper placement verified. Generally this last possibility is remote, but if the fuse-blowing began to occur immediately after work was performed on the unit, the chance of incorrect wiring as a cause is greatly increased.

SITUATION H:
Machine appears to operate satisfactorily but drips water.

The condensation of water vapor in the air is a normal by-product of air conditioning. More vapor will be condensed if the day is humid, and the amount can be surprisingly large. The condensed water collects in pans under the evaporator and condenser, most of it in the condenser pan. A device called a *slinger ring* is positioned in the pan near the condenser-fan blade. When the unit is operating, the collected water is dispersed into the atmosphere through the action of the slinger ring and fan blade. If the air is quite humid, a large amount of water will accumulate from condensation and the pan can overflow and water drip out of the exit hole. So the drip is normal. If it proves a nuisance, it can be rerouted with tubing to exit at a less objectionable spot.

If water drips into the room, the machine is most probably tilted toward the room rather than the outside, as it should. Place a level on the machine and raise the front end as necessary until the unit tilts slightly toward the outside.

If this doesn't correct the situation, check for dirt and debris in the condenser-pan exit hole and its attached tubing by pouring water into the pan and seeing whether it flows out. If it doesn't, the extension hole or tubing is clogged. The obstruction can usually be removed by pushing a straightened coat-hanger or stiff wire through the hole or tubing.

It is also possible that the drip pan may have developed a hole from corrosion. A close inspection will determine this. If a hole is present, it can be sealed by cleaning the area with a wire brush on a drill, or manually with steel wool, and filling the hole with two-part epoxy, permagum, or Heat Stik. A particularly good substance for quick sealing of water leaks when no pressure is involved is plumber's two-part epoxy putty.

4

WASHING MACHINES

Figure 88 shows a Westinghouse automatic clothes-washing machine with its top panel removed (screws around the perimeters of the various panels attach them to the frame of the machine). Many repairs detailed in the chapter were performed on this unit.

SITUATION A:

You put a load of clothes into the machine, start it, and return in an hour or so. The machine has stopped running at some point before its final cycle. In one typical case, water has remained in the tub at a level usual for the wash cycle, and the timer dial has stopped at the DRAIN position, just before SPIN.

This is the most common type of malfunction in washing machines. In the above situation, the timer dial has stopped on DRAIN, but the malfunction might just as well have occurred at some other cycle. In the vast majority of such cases, the cause of the malfunction is a defective timer.

To gain access to the timer for testing, it is necessary to remove the top of the unit. Most tops are attached with two screws at the back and spring clips in front. The clipped locations are marked by slight depressions in the joint between the top and front panel. Insert a 1-inch putty knife into the depression and push forward to disengage the clip.

When the top is removed, you can see a rod attached to the back of the timer dial (at the left in Figure 89). A second rod is attached to the timer, at the back of the machine (right). The two are joined by a coupling (Figure 91). When the dial is pushed in, a push-pull type of switch in the timer energizes a small motor that drives the timer through the complete operation. The timer energizes various other components and shuts them off at the proper time until it reaches the OFF position at the end of the wash and shuts off the machine. The average time elapsed between the start and finish of an entire wash is forty to fifty minutes, though the time will vary with different machines and models.

A typical washing-machine timer (Figure 90) will have five pairs of

FIGURE 88

FIGURE 89

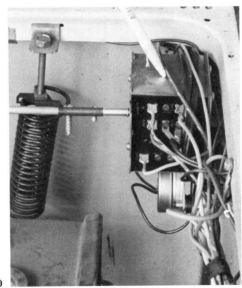

FIGURE 90

prong-type terminals. These are the ends of five switches. They operate through cams and a printed circuit and are numbered for identification. In descending order, they are: Number 4, A and B; number 2, A and B; the push-pull switch; number 3, A and B; and number 1, A and B.

Each of the switches is engaged for various periods during the wash operation. At such times its contacts are closed and the switch will evidence continuity. A typical arrangement goes as follows:

Number 1 switch will show continuity all the way through the operation except for a minute or so before the spin begins, after it ends, and before the rinse.

Number 2A switch will show continuity five minutes after the wash cycle begins and continue until thirty seconds or so before it ends. The switch's contacts will then open. They close again three minutes or so later as the spin cycles begin. The switch will then show continuity until the wash is three minutes or so from completion.

Number 2B switch (a save-and-return feature) will show continuity at the beginning of the wash cycle

until five minutes has elapsed. It will also show continuity for three minutes or so between the end of the wash cycle and the beginning of the spin. Its contacts will also close during the last three minutes.

Number 3A will evidence continuity throughout the operation except just before the end.

Number 3B will show continuity only during the spin cycles.

Number 4A will show continuity through the wash cycle, almost through the spin cycles.

Number 4B will show continuity during the spin cycles.

To test the timer, unplug the machine, remove the leads from both number 4 terminals, and prepare the continuity tester. Place one probe on the incoming hot-wire terminal and the other on the number 4B terminal. (We are determining why the machine has not gone into the spin cycles.) Rotate the timer dial from drain through spin, and if no continuity is evidenced, the timer is defective.

Each phase of the entire operation can be tested in a similar manner and the timer found functional or defective by determining whether its

switches show continuity or not during the periods when they are energized.

If the numbers 1 and 3 switches are found to be defective the switches can be removed and replaced. Numbers 2 and 4 switches are more difficult to replace. In either instance, it is simpler, easier, and not very much more expensive to replace the entire timer.

The timer and its motor are sold as a unit. It is therefore academic whether the timer is defective as the result of a bad switch or on account of its motor. New timers retail in the neighborhood of $35. Rebuilt timers, which are likely to remain functional as long as new ones, cost about $20.

To remove the defective timer, lift off all the push-on connectors attached to its terminals. Each wire is differently colored. The replacement timer will have all the various colors lettered beside its terminals to facilitate the reinstallation of leads.

The rods between the timer switch and the timer are connected by the coupling pictured in Figure 91. Remove the two screws in the coupling.

The timer and its motor are attached by two screws located at the upper right rear of the machine, directly behind the timer. Remove these screws and the timer and motor come free.

To install the new timer, reattach all the timer leads to the timer terminals, matching the colors of the wires to the colors printed beside the terminals. Fasten the two mounting screws to attach the timer and motor to the frame. Join the two rods together with the coupling by refastening the two screws removed earlier, keeping the flat sides of the rods aligned. The defective timer is now replaced.

SITUATION B:
You load clothes in the machine, start it, and return an hour or so later. The timer dial has completed its cycles, is on the OFF position, and the machine isn't running. Water is still in the tub, at a level usual for the wash cycle.

When the timer has run its course and water remains in the tub, such failure to drain may be caused by a clogged screen or drain hole, a kinked drain hose, a blocked or defective pump, a defective solenoid switch, or a defective motor. The malfunction is a common occurrence.

Before any parts are checked, the water in the tub should be removed. This is done most easily by siphoning: place a bucket in front of the machine, lay one end of a piece of tubing in the bottom of the tub and suck on the other end, then lay that end in the bucket as soon as you taste the water. This will remove all but a small amount of water.

The most frequent cause of drainage failure is a clogged screen or drain hole. Both screen and drain hole are located in the bottom center of the stationary drum in which the tub revolves. To get at them, rotate the tub so that its red *baffle* (Figure 92) lies at the bottom and center of the tub. Remove the Phillips screws around the perimeter of the baffle and it will come off.

With the baffle removed, the top of the two-part screen is visible (see Figure 93). Push both parts away from the center until the drain hole they have been covering is exposed. Remove dirt, hair, and lint from the screen and hole. If the remaining water does not drain out after the debris has been removed, the clog is further down the drainage system.

Directly below the drain hole, and

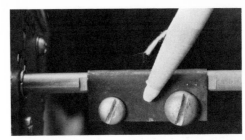

FIGURE 91

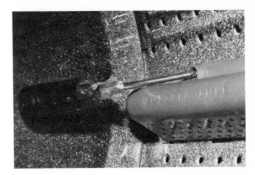

FIGURE 92

FIGURE 93

attached to it by a rubber hose, is the inlet to the *pump*. To gain access to it, either remove the front base panel, or, more simply, tilt the machine onto its back. Figure 94 shows half of the two-part pump housing, which will have to be removed in order to get to the drain inlet in the pump. It is located at the bottom of the machine, a foot or so in from the front, and is attached by seven screws around its perimeter. Place a shallow pan under the pump to catch the remaining water and remove the screws. If water begins to drip from the pump as the screws are being loosened, the failure of the water to drain is not due to a clogged screen or drain system, and other causes of the malfunction should be investigated. If only a few drops emerge as the screws are loosened, continue to remove the pump housing since a clogged drain system is now verified as the cause of the drainage failure.

Figure 95 shows the interior of the pump. At the top, directly below the center of the stationary drum, is the inlet hole. Push a straightened wire coat hanger through the pump inlet, hose, and drain hole until the remaining water in the tub drains out. The malfunction should now be corrected.

If water began to drain from the pump as its screws were being loosened, retighten the screws and examine the drain hose. It is attached to the pump outlet and continues to the drain standpipe. Without moving the machine, look for a kink or fold in the hose which would prevent the water from being pumped out. If any such restriction is present, shift the hose to remove it and the problem is solved.

If the screen, drain hole, and drain hose are not at fault, examine the *pump impeller*. The impeller (pictured in Figure 96) is attached to the motor shaft by threads. It rotates to drive the water. If it is loose, it will not spin properly and drainage will be unsatisfactory. Tighten the impeller by hand.

If the impeller is chewed up (a common occurrence), unscrew it and replace with a new impeller.

The housing has a raised circular portion and a thin, circular rubber gasket around its circumference. It also has two small projections on each side that fit into holes on the other half of the housing. During reinstallation, it is essential that the housing be in the "up" position as marked, the gasket snug against the raised circle, and the pins aligned in the holes.

From time to time the gasket will have stretched so that it does not lie tightly against the raised circumference. If it has stretched no more than $\frac{1}{4}$ inch, place the gasket in the freezer compartment of the refrigerator for an hour. This will usually shrink the gasket enough to allow it to lie tightly against the raised circumference. If the gasket has stretched more than $\frac{1}{4}$ inch, it should be replaced with a new one.

When refastening the screws of the pump housing, remember that the housing is plastic and will crack if tightening is excessive.

If none of the previous possibilities has caused the malfunction, and the machine is a General Electric late model agitator-type unit, look down between the movable and stationary drums for an article of clothing that is causing the clogging.

Failure of the machine to drain water may also be caused by the electrical component pictured in Figure 97, the pump *solenoid* switch, located at the center rear of the machine. Its function is to engage and disengage the pump. These actions are determined by the timer, which sends electricity to the solenoid or cuts it off, as required. Pumping action begins

FIGURE 94

FIGURE 96

FIGURE 95

FIGURE 97

when the pulley at the end of the pump shaft makes contact with another rotating pulley on the motor shaft. Cutoff occurs when the pulleys are separated. Both actions are caused by the pump solenoid.

To test the solenoid, unplug the machine and remove a lead from one of the solenoid's two terminals. Place the timer dial on DRAIN. Place a continuity probe on each of the solenoid terminals. Rotate the timer dial through SPIN. If no continuity is evidenced, detach the solenoid's two screws and leads and replace it.

If none of these possibilities caused the malfunction, the motor should be tested. This may be done with the direct-start cord, a test lamp, or the continuity tester. It may also be done by detaching the outgoing hot wire that runs from the timer to the motor and attaching a jumper between the hot incoming terminal of the timer and the motor terminal. When installing the jumper wire (in this situation and all others), keep it away from belts and other moving parts in which it might become entangled. Plug the machine in momentarily. If the motor runs, it is operational. If it doesn't, the motor must be replaced.

To replace a defective motor, re-move its attached leads and the bolts that secure it to the frame, and install the new motor. (Some machines will require self-evident additional steps to remove the motor.)

SITUATION C:
You load the machine with clothes, start it, and return in an hour or so. The floor is covered with water. During this time you may also have heard noises from inside the machine, like the rattling of metal in a glass jar.

This is a common malfunction that may be caused by a defective hose, an improperly attached hose, a faulty pump gasket, a hole in the stationary drum, or a cracked pump housing.

Most likely by far is a cracked pump housing caused by coins left in the pockets of clothes. Dimes in particular have a way of working themselves under the screens, through the drain hole, and into the pump. The impeller flings the coin around and creates the noises. It also scars the interior of the pump and, since the pump housing is thin plastic, will often crack it. (Within one month, I removed coins from the pump of this particular machine on five separate occasions. The last time, there was a hole in the housing the size of a pea.) The joint at the pump outlet and housing is particularly weak to begin with, and is itself highly susceptible to damages.

To check exactly where the leak is occurring, pour a quart of water into the machine and watch where it emerges. The leak may be at one point and the water dripping at another, so particular attention must be paid to determine just where the actual hole is. Most likely the water will be coming from the pump, but if there is any doubt, look at the clamps on the inlet and outlet hoses. If they have slipped down and are clamping only the hose, not the hose and the plastic pipe end inside, a leak is likely.

The clamps are the wire type and may be difficult to reposition with an ordinary pair of pliers, since the ends will slip out of the plier jaws. Wire-cutting pliers, which hold the ends of the clamp in the jaw cutout, work better. If the clamps are positioned correctly (over both hose and pipe ends), check the hoses closely for slits and, if necessary, replace.

If clamps and hoses check out, inspect the joint of the drain pipe and stationary drum. It is rare for a leak to develop in this area, but it can happen. If you suspect this possibility, pour in more water and check again. If a leak is spotted, clean the area an inch or so around the hole with a wire brush on a drill, until the metal is shiny. Dry the area thoroughly. Mix two-part epoxy and apply it over the cleaned area. Allow the repair to sit overnight.

Epoxy is the simplest means of plugging the leak, but the method can be unreliable. I have seen epoxy repairs that appeared satisfactory but then failed after a few weeks or months. The most important factor for a satisfactory epoxy repair is cleaning the area meticulously before the epoxy is applied. Welding the leak is of course preferable and should be done if the equipment is available.

If the leak is in any part of the pump, by far the most likely possibility, remove the water in the tub, unplug the machine, close the hot- and cold-water valves (located at the end of the rubber hoses), unscrew the hoses, lift the drain hose out of the drain pipe, move the machine away from the wall, and lay it on its back for easier accessibility.

Figure 98 shows the pump completely disassembled. To remove it for

FIGURE 98

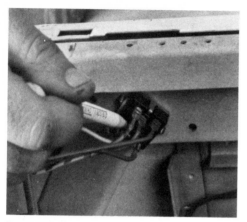

FIGURE 99

repair of its housing, first unscrew the seven screws in the front that join the two halves. If the hole or crack is on the front housing half, pull off the attached tubing; if the leak is elsewhere, the tubing need not be removed. (And of course if the leak is in view, the pump assembly needn't be taken apart.) Unscrew the impeller. Remove the nuts holding the shaft. Unscrew the pulley wheel at the opposite end of the shaft. Remove the metal arm beside the pulley, and all parts of the assembly are detached.

Clean and roughen the area approximately $\frac{1}{2}$ inch around the crack or hole by rubbing with emery cloth. Wipe clean and dry. Apply two-part epoxy over the cleaned area and allow it to set overnight.

This will usually plug the leak satisfactorily, but if the damage to the pump housing is extensive, it is best to replace the part.

SITUATION D:
You switch on the machine. Water rises above the normal level and keeps entering the tub. It stops, but the water level is abnormally high.

This condition will occur when a certain component, the *fill switch,* becomes defective. It will also occur when there is leakage of air in the tubing attached to it.

The fill switch (pictured in Figure 99) is located on the upper-right side of the machine. A length of attached plastic tubing extends to the front of the pump housing. As water enters the machine, air in the tubing is compressed and exerts pressure against a diaphragm inside the switch. At a water level preset in the factory, air pressure against the diaphragm causes the switch to trip and shut off the incoming water.

Examine the tubing for any tiny air leak around its connections, even a pinhole. (A larger leakage of air would cause water to keep entering the tube since no pressure at all would be built up.) If a defect is found in the tubing, pull it off and replace with a new length.

If the tubing is sound and securely attached, remove the fill switch by detaching its leads and two mounting screws and replace with a new switch.

A defective fill switch may also shut off water to the machine before the proper level is reached.

The fill switch is not adjustable and must be replaced when it allows too much or too little water to enter.

SITUATION E:
You start a load of wash. Water enters at a trickle and takes a long time (say six minutes or more) to reach the proper level.

This situation is fairly common. In normal operation, the tub should fill with water in two to four minutes. When it takes appreciably longer, the cause may be a hot- and/or cold-water valve only slightly open, a crimped or blocked inlet hose, a defective mixing valve, or most usually, clogged strainers.

To correct the condition, open the hot- and cold-water valves fully by turning them counterclockwise. These valves are located in the house plumbing directly behind the machine. If they are already open fully, examine the hoses and remove any sharp bends or folds by shifting or turning the affected hose.

If both valves and hoses are all right, the strainers should now be checked. These are located inside the *mixing valve* pictured in Figure 100. The mixing valve is solenoid-operated and is located in the upper-right corner at the rear of the machine. The cold- and hot-water hoses from the house water supply are attached to its

two inlets. It has an internal mixing chamber that permits a variety of water temperatures controlled through a temperature-selector dial on the face of the machine and a thermostat. A third hose connected to the outlet of the valve carries the mixed water to the tub.

To correct the condition, unscrew the hot- and cold-water inlet hoses (the couplings are similar to those of a garden hose). When the hoses have been removed, the screens, as pictured in Figure 101, become visible. If the screens are made of plastic, they can be removed easily with needle-nosed pliers, then cleaned and reinserted. (When replacing a screen, the convex side lies outward from the valve.) If the screens are metal, they cannot in many instances be removed without damage, and cleaning has to be done with the screens in place.

Cleaning the screens will ordinarily permit water to enter at a normal rate. If it still takes longer than two to four minutes to fill the tub with water, the valve itself is defective or clogged (assuming that the water pressure in the house plumbing is normal—35 pounds per square inch is average; 15 pounds is the minimum required).

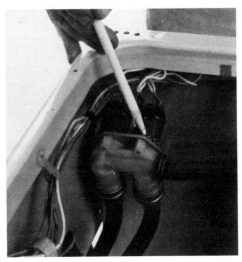

FIGURE 100

FIGURE 101

FIGURE 102

When a washing-machine component becomes defective, the simplest course ordinarily is to replace it. The faulty operation of a mixing valve, however, is usually caused by foreign matter (scale, rust, and other impurities in the incoming water) obstructing the free movement of a plungerlike part (Figure 102) that controls the admission of water, and this condition is easily corrected.

First, remove the screws that fasten the valve housing and clean the interior. Slide the plungers in their guides until they move freely. Reassemble the housing.

If this doesn't correct the condition, the defective valve must be removed and replaced. Unplug the machine and shut the hot- and cold-water valves in the house plumbing. Unscrew the two incoming hoses, loosen the clamp, and remove the outgoing hoses. Detach the leads. Remove the two mounting screws which secure the mixing valve to the frame. Install a new valve by reversing the procedure.

SITUATION F:
You start the machine but no water enters the tub.

This common malfunction will occur when the supply valves in the house plumbing have been inadvertently closed, when the inlet hoses are kinked so as to shut off the water, when the mixing-valve screens are completely clogged, or when the mixing valve or timer is defective. It will also occur in some machines equipped with a temperature selector that has an OFF position. If such a dial is in the OFF position, simply turn it to the desired temperature.

The most common cause of water failing to enter the tub is a defective timer. When the timer dial is rotated to the START position and pulled out, current is sent to the solenoid of the mixing valve through the timer. This causes the plungers to lift from their seats and admit water. If the timer is defective and no electricity is sent to the mixing valve, the plungers will remain shut and, of course, no water will enter.

To determine whether the timer is causing the malfunction, unplug the machine and prepare the continuity tester. Set the timer dial at START. Trace the red wire from the mixing valve to the timer prong. Remove the lead from the timer. Place one probe on the prong and the other on the incoming hot-wire terminal of the timer. Rotate the timer dial clockwise through about seven settings. This corresponds to the fill period. If no continuity is evidenced, the timer is defective and must be replaced.

To remove the defective timer, detach its leads and mounting screws and install a new timer.

If the timer shows continuity, check the water inlet hoses for sharp folds which would prevent water from entering the mixing valve. Reposition as needed to remove the kinks.

If the house plumbing valves are open, the timer operational, and the hoses clear, the hot- and cold-water hoses should now be detached from the mixing valve and the screens cleaned. If this doesn't correct the condition, the mixing valve should be disassembled and cleaned. If even this doesn't result in the normal admission of water, replace the mixing valve as described in the previous section.

SITUATION G:
You put in a load of wash, start the machine, return in an hour or so, and find that the clothes are soaked with water, although there is little or no additional water in the tub.

This condition develops when the machine has not gone through the spin cycles. To determine the cause, rotate the timer dial clockwise to SPIN and pull it out. If the tub doesn't spin but *you hear the motor running,* the cause of the malfunction is most likely a defective solenoid (the electrical component which engages the spinning mechanism), or a broken or slipping belt.

Figure 103 shows a portion of the back of the machine. Two belts can be seen. Examine the belt connected to the motor and tub pulleys. Assuming that the belt is not broken (in which case it should of course be replaced), there should not be more than $\frac{1}{2}$ inch of play, or the belt is likely to slip rather than drive the tub. A stretched belt may be tightened by adjustment screws which shift the motor further out, but it is usually better to replace the belt, since it will probably stretch even further with continued usage and the problem will recur.

If the belt is all right, the high-speed solenoid pictured in Figure 104 should be tested next. It is located

FIGURE 103

FIGURE 104

next to the pulley at the rear of the machine. Unplug the cord, remove one lead from its terminal, and place a tester on each of the terminals. If there is no continuity, the solenoid is defective.

To remove the defective solenoid, detach its leads and remove its two mounting screws. Install a new high-speed solenoid.

If the solenoid shows continuity, install a jumper wire between the incoming hot wire on the timer and the incoming terminal of the solenoid.

Trace the wire (often colored brown) between the timer and solenoid to determine the correct terminals. Place the timer dial on SPIN and plug the machine in briefly, no more than a few seconds. If the tub begins to spin, the timer is defective and must be replaced as previously described (see pages 70–73).

SITUATION H:

You load the machine, place the selector dial on the desired temperature, rotate the timer dial to START, and pull it out. The machine doesn't start.

When an electrical appliance fails to start, a logical assumption is that the electricity needed has been cut off. In the case of a washing machine, the possible causes are the house wiring, an unplugged or defective appliance cord, the breakdown of a safety switch that operates in conjunction with the door, or, most likely, a defective timer. (As stated previously, the timer is the component that causes most washing-machine malfunctions.)

The procedures for checking the house wiring and an appliance cord are detailed in the first chapter. They should now be followed.

If neither the house wiring nor appliance cord is the problem, a check of the *safety switch* is in order. In normal operation, the safety switch shuts off all electricity to the machine when the door is open and restores continuity when the door is closed. (It will also cut off all power when an "off balance" condition occurs. The switch is reset by raising the lid. No adjustment should be made to this switch.)

To test the switch, unplug the appliance cord and detach one of the leads to the safety switch. Prepare the continuity tester. Depress the switch manually and place a probe on each of its terminals. If no continuity is evidenced, replace the defective switch.

If the switch has continuity, turn the timer dial to START and place one probe on the incoming hot-wire terminal of the timer (Figure 105) and the other on the terminal whose outgoing wire runs to the mixing valve. If no continuity is evidenced, the timer must be replaced.

SITUATION I:

You load the machine, place the selector dial on the desired temperature, and rotate the timer dial to START and pull it out. The machine fills with water in the normal way. You later return and find that the timer dial has moved forward a few marks to the WASH position and has remained there.

This condition is most frequently caused by a defective timer and much less often by a defective motor. (It can also be caused by a defective capacitor if the unit has a capacitor.)

Use the direct-start cord, multi-tester, or test lamp to test the motor. If the motor runs or shows continuity, the timer must be replaced.

If the motor fails to run with the direct-start cord or shows a loss of continuity with the multitester or test lamp, it is defective and must be replaced.

To remove the defective motor, detach its leads, belt, and pulley, and remove the mounting bolts attaching it to the support plate. Replace with a new or rebuilt motor.

SITUATION J:
Water doesn't shut off.

This condition is most frequently caused by the failure of the timer to rotate or by sticking contacts. The condition is corrected by replacing the timer. Water will also continue to enter the tub if the inlet-valve plunger fails to seal the pilot hole in the diaphragm inside the valve. If the timer is not causing the condition, the valve should be disassembled, cleaned, and reinstalled. If the malfunction still persists, the mixing valve must be replaced.

SITUATION K:
The machine "walks."

The movement of the washer away from its location is usually due to a nonlevel installation. This can be cor-rected by placing a carpenter's level on top of the machine and adjusting the front legs so that the bubble in the level is centered in relation to both depth and width. (The rear legs are often self-leveling and need no adjustment.)

"Walking" may also occur if the load in the machine is too heavy and unbalanced. Towels and other articles that absorb a great deal of water are often the cause. The remedy is to remove some of the articles if the machine has been overloaded or redistribute them evenly around the tub.

SITUATION L:
The machine goes through its complete operation without any apparent malfunction but the washing results are unsatisfactory.

Cleaning clothes in a washing machine is accomplished by a detergent solution dissolving and loosening dirt in the fabric and by the mechanical action of flexing the clothes and forcing the detergent through their fabric.

Both cleaning actions are aided by hot, soft water, which increases the chemical action of the detergent.

FIGURE 105

The temperature of the water *in the machine* must be between 140° and 160°F for optimum results. Very often the temperature of the water delivered to the machine is lower. To correct the condition, reset the thermostat on the house water heater so that it will deliver water within the specified range.

Water that contains silt, scale, iron, and other impurities will also reduce washing efficiency. The condition is neither easily nor cheaply corrected, but if poor washes are a regular occurrence, filters in the water-supply pipes or a water-conditioning apparatus should be considered. In most instances, however, satisfactory results will be obtained if a good wash solution is provided.

Despite advertising assertions, the choice of one particular brand of detergent over another is *not* the way to achieve a good wash solution. The amount of detergent, however, is an important factor.

The proper amount of detergent cannot be determined unless the degree of water hardness is known. Hardiness varies with different localities. Call the Municipal Water Department to find out your water hardness. The recommended amount on the package of detergent will apply *only* if the water hardness is 5 to 7 grains (a grain is the unit of water hardness). If the water contains fewer grains, less detergent is needed, and if more, then more detergent is needed.

If the amount recommended on the box of detergent is 8 ounces and the water hardness is 1, the proper amount is 4 ounces. If the recommended amount on the box is 12 ounces and the water hardness is 14, 18 ounces should be used. Proportionate amounts should be used for water hardness between these two limits.

If the water hardness is between 0 and 4 grains, a low-sudsing detergent is optimum. If the water hardness is greater than 15, add $\frac{1}{4}$ cup (2 ounces) of nonprecipitating water softener for each 3-grain rise in water hardness.

For loads nine pounds and over, add $\frac{1}{4}$ cup of additional detergent. (A large or especially dirty load would need an extra $\frac{1}{2}$ cup.)

With tablets or liquid detergent, follow the package instructions if the water is 5 to 7 grains hardness. (Do not go below the minimum amount unless excessive sudsing occurs.) Increase the recommended amount about 10 percent for each grain above 7. Add $\frac{1}{4}$ cup extra for large loads and $\frac{1}{2}$ cup additional for heavily soiled, oily loads.

If the wash comes out yellowed throughout, the short-term solution is one or two hot washes with chlorine bleach added to the proper amount of detergent. The long-term solution is to raise the temperature of the water to 150°F and increase the frequency of bleaching.

If yellowing occurs over the entire article, the cause is probably water treated by a mechanical-action water softener. The short-term solution is to use chlorine bleach. The long-term solution is to decrease the amount of detergent, but not to the point of an unclean wash. In addition, the frequency of bleaching should be increased.

If yellowing is more severe in body-contact areas (but all other areas are also affected), the cause is probably hard water. To restore the article, clean with a nonprecipitating water softener. Increase the amount of detergent used and include a water softener such as New Oakite, Calgon, or Tex.

If the article is made of synthetic fabric and becomes discolored by body oil, dye pickup, or both, or if it yellows (as in the case of Nylon, Dacron, and so forth), make a paste of detergent and water and apply to the soiled areas before washing. A liquid detergent such as All, Dynamo, Wisk, or Gain, may be substituted for the paste. Pretreat the affected areas. Use the normal amount of the same detergent for washing.

General yellowing is also caused by iron or manganese in the water supply. Fabrics in such cases will respond well to dye removers such as Rit, Tintex, and so forth. The long-term solution is the installation of water conditioning and increasing the use of nonprecipitating water softeners to remove the iron from the water. It will also help to drain the hot-water heater more frequently. Chlorine bleaches *should not* be used.

Yellowing of clothing may also occur if the water supply has been colored by decayed vegetation. The articles so affected will respond well to bleaching. An increase in the amount of detergent and more frequent bleaching will also be helpful.

Phosphate detergents generally give better results than do carbonate detergents. Carbonate detergents can produce negative effects on cotton fabrics and the machine itself. Calcium carbonate (a salt) builds up on cotton fabrics, making them abrasive and accelerating fabric wear. Hot water at about 130°F is best for reducing this buildup. Oily soil removal is also optimal at this temperature.

Soaking in a mild vinegar-water solution can restore stiff, harsh-feeling fabrics. Caution should be observed, however, since the solution may strip resin from permanent-press clothes. Some dyes are also adversely affected by a vinegar solution. DO NOT use vinegar in the washer or allow it to contact other porcelain surfaces.

The addition of phosphate Calgon will help reduce the buildup of calcium carbonate in the garments, washer, and plumbing; $\frac{1}{2}$ cup (4 ounces) used once or twice a week is sufficient.

The clogging of filter pans is usually caused by the calcium carbonate found in most low- or non-phosphating detergents. The pans are best cleaned with a vinegar-water solution and a brush. Soak the filter pan in a preheated solution (160°F) of 50 percent vinegar and 50 percent water for fifteen minutes, then brush each side of the pan while flushing it with warm running water.

If the filter pan is heavily scaled, soak it overnight before brushing, and flush it with warm water while brushing. If clogging persists, soak the filter pan overnight in a solution of 2 cups of vinegar and 1 gallon of warm water. Brush and flush. This may have to be done weekly. When heating the soak-solution, do not exceed 180°F; higher temperatures may warp the filter pan. And remember not to soak in porcelain containers, or to use vinegar in or on the washer. Vinegar will cause etching and, in time, the removal of porcelain from the finished surfaces.

Probably the most common cause of an unsatisfactory wash is overloading the machine. (It is also a common cause of washer malfunctions.) The size of the tub is misleading since it is the wet weight of the clothing that is the determining factor of an overloaded machine and of poor washing results. Towels and other highly absorbent materials may occupy only a portion of the tub and still overload it.

The motor contains a protective overload which cuts off power to the motor when sudden, excessively heavy demands are made on it. Although the overload resets itself automatically, intermittent washing will produce poor results. Even if the motor operates continuously, the results will still be poor, since the necessary mechanical action is markedly reduced. The solution is to reduce the size of the load, especially if highly absorbent articles such as rugs, towels, bedspreads, etc., are being washed.

5
DISHWASHERS

Most of the repairs detailed in this chapter were performed on the Kenmore dishwasher pictured in Figure 106. It is essentially the same as all other dishwashers, both portable and under-the-counter models.

The top can be removed by unfastening the three screws along the back, then sliding the top forward until the clips attached to the underside clear the front of the metal frame.

SITUATION A:
You load and start the dishwasher. After a while you hear intermittent sounds of metal striking metal. The unit completes its operation. As you begin to unload, you see that the wash is far from satisfactory.

Every appliance produces sounds during normal operation. In a dishwasher, these sounds vary as water enters the machine, is sprayed over the contents, and drains. Sounds that are markedly different from those heard during normal operation are a clear and reliable indication that something is wrong. As soon as you notice unusual sounds, unlatch the door. This will stop the machine.

The noise will most often be caused by the tab of a pop-top can—most service calls are the result of one of these metal tabs in the wash load. Unusual sounds may also be caused by broken glass, fruit pits, or bones. Any of these may adversely affect the operation of the dishwasher or damage a part.

FIGURE 106

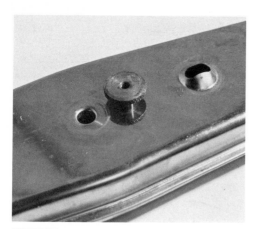

FIGURE 107

FIGURE 108

If you unlatch the dishwasher door as soon as you hear an unusual noise, the foreign object can usually be removed easily before serious damage is done to the machine. If the wash is permitted to continue, the risk of damage increases.

To get a really satisfactory wash, water must be sprayed over all the objects in the dishwasher a number of times. This is accomplished in part through a rotating *spray arm,* called an *impeller* in some machines. If the object becomes wedged between the spray arm (pictured in Figure 107) and the shaft on which it is mounted, the arm will jam and stop rotating, preventing the water from reaching all corners of the dishwasher.

You should be able to rotate the spray arm with a light flick of the finger. If more force is required or if the arm is frozen, it will have to be removed. To do this, first unload the machine and slide out the bottom tray. The upper basket is mounted on a shaft with a hole near its end. A cotter pin goes through the hole to keep the basket from falling. To remove the basket, straighten the ends of the cotter pin with pliers, tap the pin partially out of the hole, then re-move it with the pliers while holding the basket. Now lower the basket from the shaft and remove it.

Unscrew the nut located at the top center of the spray arm and lift it off. The object causing the spray arm to bind will now be visible and removable with pliers. (Needle-nosed pliers usually work well.)

If the spray arm rotates freely but the wash is unsatisfactory (and the machine has been operating normally before this), the part directly below the spray arm should be examined.

Figure 108 shows the parts that lie below the spray arm. Pictured in Figure 109 is the housing below the spray arm, the part damaged by the foreign object. A significant amount of water was ejected from the hole and crack rather than from the spray arm, causing an inferior wash. The part must be replaced.

If the tab wasn't visible when the arm was removed, it is now necessary to remove the housing. First remove the nut located on top of the housing (see Figure 110). Next remove the bolts that lie around the circumference of the housing (such as in Figure 111) and lift off the housing.

Directly beneath the housing is the

FIGURE 109

FIGURE 110

FIGURE 111

FIGURE 112

FIGURE 113

FIGURE 114

FIGURE 115

guide, pictured in Figure 112, the part that aims the water. Figure 113 shows the bottom of the same part. The curved projections along the perimeter channel the water to the spray arm. If the tab is still not accessible for removal, lift off the guide.

The blade shown in Figure 114 is the last part of the assembly. If you have not yet discovered the foreign object, it will either be here or directly below; in the latter case, you will have to lift out the blade. Pictured in Figure 115 is the inside bottom of the machine with the assembly completely removed. It is the last possible place where the foreign object could have lodged.

SITUATION B:
You load the machine, depress the button for the desired cycle, turn the timer dial to START, but nothing happens.

This situation can be due to faulty house wiring, a defective appliance cord, a wall switch in the OFF position, a door handle that is not fully closed, the misalignment of a part within the handle, a defective inlet valve, a defective motor, or, most likely, a defective timer.

When any appliance fails to start, you should always check the house wiring (the procedure is detailed in chapter 1). But first, while you're still at the dishwasher, check the door handle to make sure it is latched securely. The latched door completes the path of electricity between the timer and its small motor.

If the door handle is latched and the house wiring is all right, a defective *timer* is most likely preventing the machine from starting. The timer is located inside the door directly behind the cycle dial. To expose it for testing, first remove the small Phillips screw under the handle knob, then remove the knob. Next remove the screws on the sides of the top panel.

With the control panel lowered, the timer (on the right in Figure 116) will be accessible. Figure 117 gives a closer view of the timer. The numerous leads attached to it seem complicated at first, but with some careful study the basic arrangement becomes clear.

The timer is essentially a collection of switches. First establish which lead is the incoming hot wire. Since power is routed through the door switch, follow the outgoing lead from the

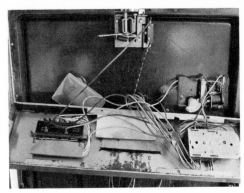

FIGURE 116

FIGURE 117

latch to the timer, noting the terminal to which it is connected. It is usually the larger terminal, with several other wires attached to it.

All remaining wires are outgoing; they are color-keyed for easier identification. Each one goes to a different component. We are interested in the one that leads to the water-inlet solenoid valve. The valve is located at the bottom front of the machine and is connected to the house hot-water supply line, usually by ⅜-inch copper tubing. Remove the bottom panel by unfastening the screws on each side and note the color of the wire running to one of the valve's two terminals.

Prepare the continuity tester and turn the dishwasher dial to START. Remove from the timer the colored lead that matches the one running to the inlet valve, and place a probe on the terminal. Place the second probe on the incoming hot-wire terminal. Shut and latch the door. If no continuity is evidenced, the timer is defective and must be replaced.

To remove the timer, first detach all of its leads by simply pulling them off the prongs of the timer. Next pull off the timer dial, if necessary, first loosening a screw set in its hub. Then remove the two mounting screws that attach the timer to the panel.

Indicated beside each terminal of the replacement timer is the color of the lead that should be attached to it. Reattach all leads, mount the timer to the panel with the two screws removed earlier, and replace the dial.

If continuity is evidenced when the timer is tested, check the inlet valve next. Remove one of its leads and place a probe of the continuity tester on each of the inlet-valve terminals. If no continuity is registered on the instrument, the valve is defective and must be replaced. (A defective inlet solenoid valve will often evidence charring along its outer coil cover.)

To replace the inlet valve, first shut off all water to the dishwasher by closing the valve on the hot-water supply (the dishwasher doesn't have a cold-water supply). This valve is normally located under the adjacent sink, but in some installations it will be found directly behind the dishwasher. Remove the two screws that attach the lower panel. The incoming hot-water line is attached to the valve with either a flared or pressure fitting. (It should never be a soldered fitting, since the heat produced during

soldering may damage the valve.) Detach the inlet and outgoing fittings. Then detach the two leads from the valve and remove the two screws that fasten the valve to its mounting plate. The valve is now free. Install its replacement by reversing the procedure.

If both the timer and inlet valve show continuity, attach the alligator clips of a two-wire direct-start cord to the two motor leads or terminals. Switch on the cord momentarily. If the motor doesn't start, it is defective and must be replaced. If the motor does start, the switch that operates it in conjunction with the door latch should be examined.

Pictured in Figure 118 is the door-latching mechanism. A push-button switch similar to the one which controls the interior light of a refrigerator is engaged when the latch is moved completely to the right. The arm of the mechanism depresses the push button. If the arm does not depress the button, loosen the latch screw and shift the arm so that it lies directly on the button, then retighten the screws.

If the mechanism is operating properly, detach a lead from the switch, place a probe on each of its terminals, and depress the button. If no continuity is evidenced, the switch is defective and must be replaced.

SITUATION C:
The machine goes through its washing operation without unusual noises or leaks, but the dishes are not properly washed.

Despite advertising claims, an unsatisfactory wash is not caused by an inferior detergent, and therefore, the condition will certainly not disappear if another brand is used. However, the use of soap powder instead of detergent will lead to an unsatisfactory wash.

A less-than-perfect wash may also occur if the items to be washed are not properly loaded. Every new dishwasher comes with a booklet showing how the machine should be loaded for optimum results. Follow the recommendations. Be particularly careful not to place pot handles or other similar items where they can obstruct the rotation of the spray arm.

Insufficiently hot water is another very common cause of an unsatisfactory wash. A dishwasher, like a washing machine, works best when the temperature of the water is between 140° and 160°F. This temperature range refers to the water *actually used* in the dishwasher and not what emerges from the hot-water heater. In one- and two-family homes the heater is often located in the basement or garage; from there the water must travel some distance before it enters the dishwasher. This allows the water to cool, and it is not uncommon for water leaving a heater at 140°F to arrive at the dishwasher at 120°F or even lower.

To determine the temperature of the water, open the hot-water tap of the sink, allow the water to run for a bit, then fill a thermos and use a thermometer to determine the temperature of the water. If it is too low, raise the temperature of the thermostat on the hot-water heater to a minimum of 145°F. This adjustment should allow for the distance to the dishwasher and for the water sitting and cooling in the pipe between heater and washer before the dishwasher is activated.

Although there is little likelihood of persuading the landlord in an old apartment building to raise the hot

FIGURE 118

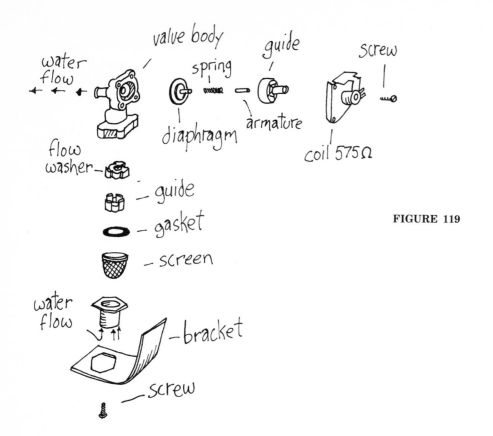

water flow

valve body

spring

guide

screw

diaphragm

armature

flow washer

coil 575Ω

— guide

— gasket

— screen

water flow

— bracket

— screw

FIGURE 119

other water-consuming appliance while the dishwasher is running will often lower the temperature of the water going to the dishwasher. It is therefore reasonable to minimize other hot water outlays while the dishwasher is in use.

Precleaning dishes and pots is also necessary. Misleading advertisements for new dishwashers have created the false belief that some miraculous discoveries incorporated into the new machines make it possible to load items directly from the dinner table into the machine. No such miraculous discoveries have been made, and precleaning before loading is still essential for optimum results.

Insufficient water can also cause an unsatisfactory wash. Most dishwashers will operate satisfactorily with between 15 and 45 pounds of water pressure per square inch and 1 to 2 gallons of water per minute, as controlled by a washer in the water-intake valve. Sometimes, but rarely, the pressure of the water supply drops below 15 pounds per square inch, resulting in an insufficient amount of water. Correcting this condition is beyond the scope of this book.

An insufficient amount of water

water temperature, you can get a small holding tank capable of supplying adequate amounts of hot water to the dishwasher. (Remember that a dishwasher uses less water than is

normally used washing the same items in a sink.)

In many dwellings, even when the water temperature is adequate to begin with, using a tub, sink, or an-will also result if the strainer in the inlet valve becomes clogged with rust, minerals, or other impurities. To get at the strainer for cleaning, first shut off the hot-water supply valve. Remove the two screws at the sides of the bottom panel to obtain access to the inlet valve, usually located a few inches behind the panel. Detach the inlet tubing from the valve by unscrewing the coupling nut. The screen is now exposed and can be cleaned. (In some installations a nipple will remain in the valve and must also be removed.) When replacing the nipple, wrap the threads $\frac{1}{2}$ inch up with plumber's tape, a plastic product used in place of pipe dope in order to prevent leaks.

Figure 119 shows a typical inlet valve completely disassembled. During reassembly the screen must be positioned with its convex side facing outward.

If cleaning the screen doesn't remedy the condition, remove the outlet hose (held by a wire clamp) and the mounting screws, then disassemble the valve for further cleaning. Push down the guide and armature to make sure that the diaphragm isn't jammed. If the diaphragm is locked in

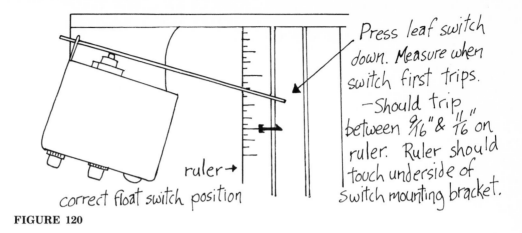

ruler→

correct float switch position

Press leaf switch down. Measure when switch first trips. —Should trip between $\frac{9}{16}$" & $\frac{11}{16}$" on ruler. Ruler should touch underside of switch mounting bracket.

FIGURE 120

a partially open position, only a small amount of water will enter the machine. It may not be possible to correct this condition, in which case the entire valve must be replaced.

Insufficient water and consequently unsatisfactory wash may also be caused by a defective *float switch* (not present on all machines). The switch shuts off power to the water-valve coil and puts the dishwasher into automatic pump-out in case of overfill, but it will not offer overfill protection if the water valve is stuck open when

the motor stops at the beginning of the DRY cycle.

Figure 120 shows the correct position of the float switch. When the switch leaf is pressed down, it should trip between $\frac{9}{16}$ inch and $\frac{11}{16}$ inch, as measured by a ruler touching the underside of the switch-mounting bracket. If the switch doesn't trip within these limits, remove the switch assembly from the dishwasher to adjust it. Hold the ruler even with the top of the bracket and one inch from the center of the hole. Bend the

FIGURE 121

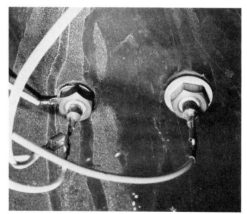

FIGURE 122

leaf so that the switch trips between $\frac{1}{4}$ inch and $\frac{3}{8}$ inch.

If this doesn't correct the condition, or if the dishwasher doesn't admit any water at all, place the probes of the continuity tester on the switch's terminals. If no continuity is evidenced, replace the float switch. If the switch shows continuity and trips properly, check the standpipe (the pipe holding the hose that runs from the sink) for foreign material that could cause the float to bind.

If the standpipe has no obstructions, place a tester probe at each end of the wire that connects the switch to the timer. Rotate the timer dial from START to the beginning of the drying cycle. If no continuity is evidenced, the timer must be replaced.

SITUATION D:
The dishwasher runs through its operation, apparently normally, but the dishes haven't dried.

This condition is caused by either a defective timer, a defective heating element, a faulty drain pump, a leaking inlet valve, a faulty blower system, or water that isn't hot enough.

The *Calrod* (Figure 121) provides the heat required to dry the dishes. It is a loop consisting of a tough outer covering and an inner wire made of a nickel-chrome alloy (nichrome). The timer delivers electricity to the nichrome wire as the drying cycle begins. Resistance to the flow of electricity through the wire creates heat, which is transferred to the outer covering and from there to the tub and its contents. Calrods are ordinarily rated between 600 and 1,000 watts, depending on the machine.

A Calrod element will start to go if a break occurs in its outer covering. Such a break may begin as a small nick caused by a pop-top or bottle cap. With the machine's continued use, the nick develops into a rupture and the exposed nichrome wire breaks, at which point continuity is lost, no resistance is encountered by the electricity, and there is no heat to dry the dishes. Breaks in the wire can also be caused by a manufacturing defect or continuous everyday use.

The Calrod terminals are located outside of the tub under the machine. They pass through the tub and are fastened with watertight fittings as displayed in Figure 122.

To check for a defective element, unplug the machine; remove one of the leads on the Calrod terminal, prepare the continuity tester, and place a probe on each of the terminals. If any continuity is evidenced, the element *is effective.* An element will almost always be either bad or good— nothing in between. If there is doubt about the continuity reading, plug in the machine, turn the timer dial to the drying cycle, and check the wattage with the amprobe watt-meter.

If no continuity is evidenced, the Calrod element must be replaced. To remove a defective element, detach its leads and unscrew the fittings on each end. When installing a new element, it is important that the nut that lies directly against the outer surface of the tub be sufficiently tightened so that the small metal projections on its face dig into the metal of the tub. This assures adequate grounding and is part of the safety system in the unit.

If the element shows continuity, it will still not provide heat if the timer is defective and thus fails to furnish the element with electricity. To determine if the timer is functioning properly, place the dial at the beginning of the drying cycle. Prepare the continuity tester. Note the color of the incoming lead to the Calrod terminal. Locate the lead of the same color on an outgoing terminal of the timer and detach it. Place one probe on this terminal and the other on the timer's incoming hot-wire terminal. Rotate the dial through the drying cycle. Continuity must be evidenced throughout the rotation or the timer is defective and must be replaced. (The procedure for replacing a defective timer has been detailed previously.)

If both the Calrod and timer are functioning properly, the *drain pump* should be investigated next.

Normally, the drain pump will pump water from the dishwasher through the drain tubing into a "dishwasher tee," a junction installed above the sink trap. While this is happening, you will hear the water gurgling, but then these noises should stop and the sounds of the pump should *continue* for a brief period before the new cycle begins. If gurgling is heard as the new cycle begins, the pump has not removed all the water.

Such pump failure is usually caused by restrictions in the sump (the depression that holds the water at the bottom of the machine) or around the impeller, and rarely by the pump itself. Cleaning in these areas has been detailed previously.

The pump will also fail to remove all the water if it is sucking air from a leak. Look for water on the floor by the dishwasher, then examine the entire pump assembly for a crack in the housing, a defective gasket, a slit in a hose, or a loose clamp.

If close examination fails to reveal any defect, start the machine and allow it to go through its initial spray cycle. Look for dripping water. The machine may have to go through several cycles before the leak can be pinpointed. If necessary, reposition a clamp or replace a defective hose. If the leak or sucking of air is caused by a break in the pump housing, remove the pump, clean and roughen the surface of the housing for an inch or so around the break, apply two-part epoxy, and allow it to sit overnight before reinstallation.

The visual and running test just outlined should be performed on the dishwasher even if a leak has not dripped any water on the floor. The hissing sound of air being sucked into

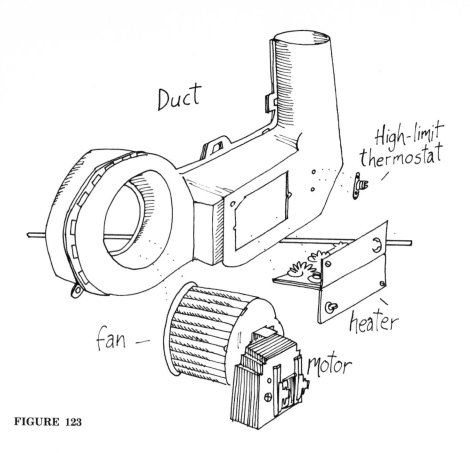

Duct

High-limit
thermostat

fan —

heater

motor

FIGURE 123

Pictured in Figure 123 is a typical heater-blower system, used in some dishwasher models. It consists of a small motor and a squirrel-cage blower that directs the air over a small nichrome wire heating element. The blower circulates hot air into the tub and over the dishes during the drying cycle. The entire blower system is usually held by two $\frac{5}{16}$-inch screws attached to a bracket welded to the tub skirt assembly. A high-limit safety thermostat mounted on the blower housing shuts off power to the heater should the blower motor stall or fail to start.

The blower motor, a shaded-pole type, is typically rated at 3 amperes and 27 watts. The heater coil is 550 watts. To test the motor, attach the two-wire direct-start cord to the terminals and briefly switch it on. If the motor fails to run, it is defective and must be replaced.

To test the heater, place a probe of the continuity tester on each of its terminals. If continuity is obtained, the element is intact and working. If no continuity is evidenced, the heater is defective and must be replaced.

If the heater is functional, test the thermostat for continuity. For it to be functional, it should evidence continu-

the pump assembly will usually pinpoint a non-dripping leak.

The bleed hole in the diaphragm washer of the water-inlet valve is supposed to prevent an excess of water in the dishwasher tub (espe-

cially when the water valve becomes defective). If the bleeder clogs, water will leak into the dishwasher. Dismantling and cleaning the water intake valve has been described previously.

ity up to 210°F plus or minus 10°F. If it shows a lack of continuity, it is defective and must be replaced.

The blower system will not operate if the timer is faulty and fails to deliver electricity when required. To test the timer, first note the color of the blower motor's incoming lead. Find the opposite end of the lead on the timer's outgoing terminal and detach it. Place the timer dial at the start of the drying cycle. Place one probe of the continuity tester on the outgoing timer terminal and the other on the incoming hot-wire terminal. Rotate the timer through the drying cycle. If continuity is evidenced, the fault lies elsewhere. If no continuity is shown, the timer must be replaced.

The blower system will also fail to operate if there is a faulty push-button switch. Test the switch for continuity in the ON position to determine if it is defective and requires replacement.

The blower system will also fail to operate if the option switch is pushed in for NATURAL DRY, since this removes the blower system from the drying operation.

The entire blower system is sold as a complete assembly and the failure of any component will necessitate a complete replacement. (An adjustment in cost will usually be made if the defective blower system is returned.)

SITUATION E:
The dishwasher operates satisfactorily at times, but at other times the wash is poor. Sometimes the machine won't operate at all.

This condition is likely to be caused by low voltage. Voltage represents the pressure of electricity. When it drops below the normal range of 110 to 120 volts, the operation of the machine is adversely affected. If it rises or falls significantly more than 10 percent from the norm, the machine may not run at all.

A reduction in voltage may stem from the utility company, but this situation is usually temporary. And when the utility company decides to drop voltage because of high demand and insufficient supply of electricity (as on hot summer days), public announcements will usually accompany the decision. The dishwasher should not be used during these "peak" hours. More often, however, low voltage is caused by the use of other appliances on the same circuit as the dishwasher, and not by the utility company.

To test the voltage, prepare the multitester as if it were to be used for continuity, but place the selector switch at 250v, two switch marks below the RX1 position. Place a probe on each of the outlet slots that supply power to the dishwasher and read the voltage on the red scale marked AC.

The test should be made when other appliances or lights on the same circuit as the dishwasher are being used. (To determine whether they are on the same circuit, remove the fuse or switch off the breaker in the main that allows the dishwasher to operate. All appliances and lights on the same circuit will then fail to work.)

A temporary solution to low voltage is to put no other demands on the circuit to which the dishwasher is connected while it is running, or to operate it from an outlet on a circuit that has less demands on it. A permanent solution is to install a new electrical line for the dishwasher. Building codes require a separate circuit in new construction, and most manufacturers insist on a separate line for their appliances, but in practice, except for a refrigerator or stove, this is rarely done. Nor is it necessary. If

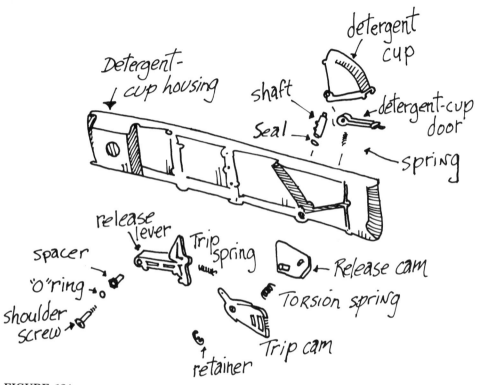

Detergent-cup housing

detergent cup

shaft

Seal

detergent-cup door

spring

release lever

Trip spring

spacer

"o" ring

Release cam

shoulder screw

Torsion spring

retainer

Trip cam

FIGURE 124

#12 wire and a 20-amp fuse are used for a line, two appliances or their equivalent can go on its circuit with plenty of electricity to spare. (Each new line has a practical capacity of 1,800 to 1,900 watts; a 110-volt dish-

washer will rarely use more than 1,000 watts.)

SITUATION F:
When you start to remove the contents in the dishwasher after a wash, you

see that the results are poor. The detergent-cup door has remained shut, with most of the detergent powder still in it.

Pictured in Figure 124 is an exploded view of the *detergent-cup assembly*. The cup cover (molded in one piece) encloses the vent and provides a mounting for the rinse-agent injector. The cup has a fifty-gram capacity and is marked at 30 grams for water that is not more than 10 grains hardness and detergents which are not low-phosphate. When the cup cover fails to trip or trips sluggishly, a poor wash results. If the cup leaks detergent, it will produce milky-white glassware.

If the cup fails to trip, remove the screws that attach the front panel. Look for a broken or missing detergent cam and make sure that all parts (as shown in the drawing) are present.

Try moving the cup shaft. If it binds, disassemble and clean all parts. Remove any caked-on detergents from the shafts or cup housing. Lubricate the shaft "O" ring with rinse-agent fluid and reassemble the shaft.

Close the cup and turn the control

dial slowly. The cup door will usually trip shortly after the fourth water fill.

When loading the machine, be careful not to place objects so that they interfere with the operation of the detergent cup.

To determine if the cup leaks detergent, fill it and start the dishwasher. Stop it every few minutes and examine the detergent in the cup. Some dampness is normal, but if the powder is almost liquid, or if the amount decreases each time the machine is stopped and inspected, the cup is leaking and should be replaced.

If 85 percent of the original powder remains just before the trip point, the leakage is not excessive and should not cause any problem.

When reinstalling the detergent cup, it is necessary to position the pin on the outside of the cam as shown in Figure 125.

SITUATION G:
You get poor washing results, mainly streaks and spots on glasses and dishes.

This condition is caused by a defective *rinse-agent dispenser* and not the particular brand of rinse being used.

Thus the rinse-agent dispenser must be repaired.

At the beginning of the final rinse, the dispenser automatically releases the required quantity of wetting agent into the rinse water. The resulting solution breaks the surface tension of the water and prevents the formation of streaks and spots on dishes and glasses.

The dispenser tank has a capacity of approximately 4 ounces, which is sufficient for 25 washings. It is designed so that when the dishwasher door is closed, a scoop directs the correct amount of wetting solution to the measuring chamber.

At the beginning of the wash, a premeasured amount of solution is ready to be released. During the final rinse, a *bimetal activator* is placed in the circuit with the Calrod element. This causes the bimetal to heat and rise, unseating the rubber-tipped valve pin in the measuring chamber, which then releases the liquid into the dishwasher.

The turbulent action of the water distributes the wetting agent. (See Figures 126, 127.)

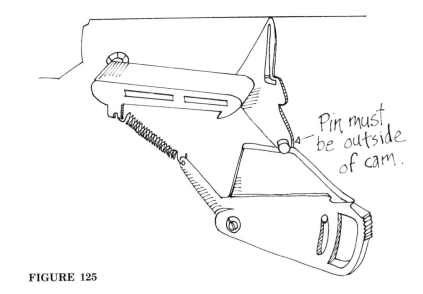

FIGURE 125

FIGURE 126

when door is open

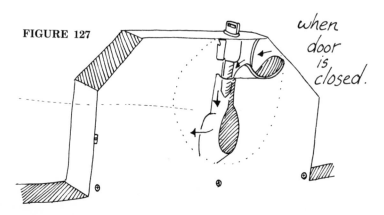

FIGURE 127

when door is closed.

Figure 128 shows the valve when closed, Figure 129 when opened.

The dispenser cover is heat-sealed to the dispenser body and cannot be separated, but the bimetal activator, pin-valve, and filler cap are all sold as separate components.

The bimetal strip has an adjusting screw, which maintains enough pressure on the strip to prevent it from shifting and unseating the valve during the wash cycle. Normally, it touches the lower surface of the opening at the top of the valve pin. Positioned this way, it permits the strip to activate slightly without unseating the valve, which would cause the wetting agent to leak before the final rinse.

To adjust the bimetal strip to its proper position, first remove it from the rinse-agent tank. Hold the adjusting screw with a screwdriver and loosen the locknut as pictured in Figure 130. Lay the bimetal assembly on a flat surface and turn the adjusting screw so that the end of the strip barely touches the flat surface. Tighten the locknut and reattach it to the tank.

If the wetting agent is still not being released properly, place the probes of the continuity tester on the bimetal terminals. If no continuity is evidenced, replace the strip. If continuity is evidenced, check for continuity of the switch in the timer that connects the bimetal in the circuit with the Calrod. (This can be identified by tracing the wire from the bimetal through the Calrod and to the timer's outgoing terminal.) The timer dial should be rotated through the release phase with one probe on the incoming hot-wire terminal and the other on the outgoing terminal (to the Calrod and bimetal). If no continuity is evidenced, the timer is defective and must be replaced.

SITUATION H:
Water leaks from the dishwasher.

Leaks from the machine can occur because of a leaking pump, a defective inlet valve, a misaligned fill switch, a defective measuring coil, a defective door gasket, a loose nut in the fitting between the copper inlet tubing and the inlet valve, or a clogged drain.

The procedures for determining the operability, adjustment, repair, or replacement of the pump, inlet valve, fill switch, and measuring coil have been explained previously.

The door gasket is a one-piece

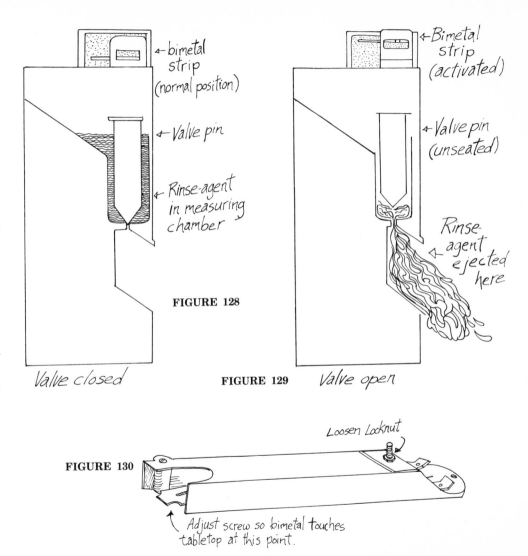

FIGURE 128

Valve closed

FIGURE 129　Valve open

FIGURE 130

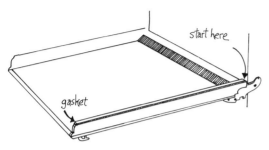

start here

gasket

FIGURE 131

extruded-vinyl part that fits into a slot molded into the inner-door panel. A close examination of the gasket will usually reveal whether it is causing the leak. If the gasket is bunched, deformed (swollen), lifted out of position, cut, or worn, it must be replaced or repositioned.

To remove the defective gasket, pull it directly out of its retainer slot. It is not necessary to remove the dishwasher door. Usually there are no holding clips or cement to keep the gasket in the slot; some gaskets are attached with screws while others fit into a groove and are held by a retaining clip fastened with screws.

Position the new gasket on either side of the door, near the bottom, as pictured in Figure 131. Press it into the start of the slot. Continue around

the door and press into place several inches at a time. There should be from 2 to $2\frac{1}{2}$ inches between the end of the gasket strip and the bottom of the door.

The hot water connection to the inlet valve is usually a flared or pressure fitting. The vibration of the machine may in time cause the nut to loosen. To check for a leak, remove the two screws that hold the bottom panel and start the machine. If water drips at the fitting, tighten the nut. This is often all that is needed to stop the leak, especially with a flared fitting.

If you're working with a pressure fitting, tightening the nut may cause the leak to grow. If it does, completely remove the nut and slide it back on the tubing.

Pressure fittings contain a ferrule— a small ring-shaped, partially tapered brass piece. The inside of the ferrule is roughly the same diameter as the outside of the copper tubing. It fits over the tubing and into the nut. If the tubing is not aligned with the valve fitting for at least 1 inch, chances are that the ferrule will not be properly seated, and as the nut is tightened, a portion of the ferrule will emerge from the back of the nut. If

this occurs, no amount of tightening will stop the leak.

To stop the leak, purchase a $\frac{3}{8}$-inch ferrule in a hardware store, bend the tubing so that it aligns with the inlet of the valve for at least 1 inch, slip the ferrule over the tubing, and gradually tighten the nut. If any portion of the ferrule begins to appear behind the nut, loosen the connection and reposition the ferrule before it is deformed by further tightening.

A clogged drain will usually cause an excess of water in the tub, and leakage will occur even if the door gasket is intact. The first section of this chapter details how to disassemble the water system to relieve clogging.

When the drain water leaves the pump, it travels through a rubber hose $\frac{1}{2}$ inch in diameter which is connected to the house drain above the sink trap. Occasionally water will fail to drain from the tube because of hose kinking or blockage, and the accumulated excess water will cause a leak. The hose is held by clamps at each end and is easily removed. Very often the drain hose also has a U-shaped piece of aluminum through which the drain water passes. It prevents sink waste from backing into the dishwasher and water from siphoning out of the dishwasher. If there is such a U, it is held by clamps which should be removed to facilitate cleaning the hose. Insert a length of wire through the drain hose to clear any obstruction, then run tap water through each section of hose to make sure it flows freely.

If neither the drain, nut, or gasket is responsible for the leak, the dishwasher should be tested to see if too much water is being admitted. The amount of water needed to operate a dishwasher satisfactorily varies with models and makes. The following procedure should be suited to most models:

Place 21 pints of water into the empty machine and mark the side of the tub at the resulting water level. Start the machine. Allow it to run until a 90-second fill cycle has been completed. (Some models use a 17-pint, 77-second fill cycle.) You can hear the water entering and being shut off. Open the door and compare the water level to the mark previously made. Variation of an inch or so is acceptable, since water metering in these machines in not exact.

If the water level indicates an excess of seven or eight pints, refer

back to the beginning of this section to check out the components that could be causing leakage.

SITUATION I:
The door seems to have sagged and the latch mechanism won't lock or locks with difficulty.

Difficulty with the latch mechanism occurs when the door is seated too high or low. It can be adjusted up or down to align the latch compartment with the latch. The door hinges are one-piece stampings held to the door with hex-head screws. A hook on one

end of the hinge is connected to the door spring.

To adjust the door, remove the front panel and loosen the two screws in the hinge to be adjusted, as shown in Figure 132. Raise or lower the door so that the keeper engages the latch without difficulty, then retighten the screws. (The maximum possible adjustment is between $\frac{1}{4}$ inch and $\frac{1}{2}$ inch.)

SITUATION J:
Dishwasher runs continuously.

This condition is caused by a defective timer or, much more often, by inad-

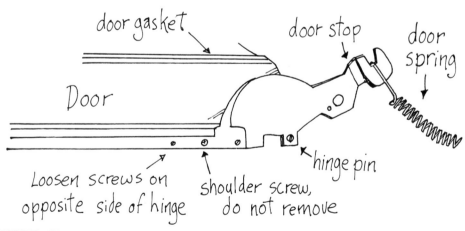

FIGURE 132

vertently placing the push-button switch in a "neutral" position. Many push-button switches are very sensitive. Accidental halfway contact can cause the switch to assume some continuity but not enough to activate it fully. In this in-between position, the dishwasher will behave erratically.

To correct the condition in machines with full switch features, press the CANCEL AND DRAIN button and wait five minutes. Then depress the NORMAL SOIL button. Press the PUSH TO START button and start the dishwasher. In most cases this will restore normal operation. It will also frequently correct malfunctions evidenced by water left in the tub, poor washes, or blackened silverware.

If the procedure doesn't correct the condition, unplug the machine and place the timer dial in the OFF position. Prepare the continuity tester. Place one probe on the incoming hot-wire terminal. Remove a lead from the on-off switch and place the other probe on the terminal. If continuity *is* evidenced, the on-off switch in the timer must be replaced.

SITUATION K:
Everything seems to be working all right but a good deal of water remains behind the front panel and the wash is unsatisfactory.

The problem is most likely water condensation. It can be greatly reduced in the following manner:

Remove the access and color-back panels from the door. Cut the insulation in the access panel in half and stuff one half into the door channel on each side. Reinstall the access and main-door panels.

SITUATION L:
As situation K, but instead of water behind the front panel there are droplets clinging to the top of the tub.

Droplets clinging to the top of the tub will spatter onto the dishes as they dry and cause an unsatisfactory wash. To prevent droplets from forming, wet a scouring pad that has *no soap* in it and rub the top of the tub, giving each portion 15 to 20 strokes. Press the RINSE AND HOLD button and start the dishwasher. In approximately 10 minutes, the cycle will end. Check the tub top. If droplets remain, treat the area again with the scouring pad.

SITUATION M:
You load and start the machine. The motor sounds louder than usual and may shut off completely, then go on again in a few minutes.

When unusual sounds come from the motor, or if it turns off on its own before the wash is complete, even if it starts running again by itself, it is behaving abnormally and should be checked.

Fill the machine with 21 pints of water. Rotate the timer dial to DRAIN, a few marks before DRY. Attach an amprobe around one of the two leads in the appliance cord and start the machine. Let it run for a couple of minutes and read the amperage draw. (This figure is given for a loaded machine, which is why it is necessary to fill the machine with water.) If the amperage draw is over 15 percent higher than the figure on the nameplate, the motor is defective and, even though it continues to run, must be replaced. (Even if only the internal overload is defective, it is necessary to replace the entire motor.)

SITUATION N:
Motor fails to run.

The simplest way to test a motor is with the direct-start cord. The motor in the dishwasher has two leads. Attach the two-wire direct-start cord to the motor leads or motor terminals and plug it in. Turn on the switch for a couple of seconds. If the motor runs, the previous failure was most likely caused by the timer. If the motor fails to run, it is defective and must be replaced.

The motor may also be checked with the continuity tester if a direct-start cord isn't handy.

In addition to its continuity, the grounding of the motor should be checked. Unplug the machine and detach the leads to the motor. Prepare the continuity tester in the usual way. Scrape away a small area of the motor housing surface with a kinfe so that some bare metal is exposed. Place one probe on the bare metal and the other on the end of a motor lead or terminal. *Both* leads or terminals must be tested; if *either* shows continuity, the motor is internally grounded and must be replaced.

SITUATION O:
You receive a shock when you touch the machine.

This occurs because the machine is not grounded properly. It usually happens when the screw fastening the green grounding wire in the appliance cord to the frame of the machine becomes loose and the wire breaks contact with the metal surface. To locate the screw, trace the appliance cord from where it enters the machine until you find where the grounding wire separates from the rest of the cord, then follow the wire to its end. Retightening the screw will usually restore the grounding and eliminate shocks.

There are several groundings in addition to the one described above, and if shocks persist, these connections should be examined. The first is the outlet into which the machine is plugged, which should have a round hole for grounding in addition to the usual two slots. To check the outlet, first remove the corresponding fuse in the main or switch the breaker to OFF, then remove the outlet's coverplate and the two screws located at the top and bottom of the receptacle. Pull the receptacle out of its box. The green hex screw on the receptacle is for grounding. One end of a short, bare copper wire should be attached to it; the wire's other end should be attached to a second screw at the back of the box for secure contact with metal.

Also examine the mounting nuts that attach the Calrod. They should be forcefully tightened so that their burrs dig into the metal of the tub and provide good grounding.

Other grounding locations are given on the wiring diagram attached to the machine. If shocks persist, all designated locations must be checked and the necessary screws tightened to eliminate the condition.

SITUATION P:
The machine runs independently in respect to the timer dial position. You receive a shock when you touch the machine.

Both of these symptoms occur when the polarity of the machine has been reversed, usually after there has been a short. The machine will operate, but not under the control of the timer, and its activity will be very erratic. The machine must be regrounded before it will run properly.

GENERAL INFORMATION

A perfectly sound dishwasher may produce unsatisfactory results because of inadequate information or instruction on its use.

Dishwasher owners frequently complain about broken or chipped dinner-ware, particularly fine bone or porce-lain china. When dishes of the same size are loaded next to one another, water turbulence will force their rims together and cause chipping or break-age. To prevent this from happening, separate dishes of the same size by alternating them with smaller plates.

Recently manufactured fine-patterned china is usually machine washable (older patterns most often are not, so check before washing), but colors will fade with continued expo-sure to alkaline washing solutions. To prolong color life, decrease the washing time when machine washing all fine china.

Plastic dinnerware is made from two basic types of plastic, thermoset-ting and thermoplastic. Thermoset-ting plastic (such as Melamine) is tasteless and odorless and will not soften or contort when heated. Ther-moplastic dinnerware does become soft and loses its shape when exposed to high heat. It should be washed on the top rack, farthest from the Calrod element. Chlorine bleaches, scouring cleansers, and scouring pads should *never* be used on plastic; once the sur-face is scratched, it will stain more

quickly and deeply, shortening the life of the dinnerware.

Coffee and other food stains will eventually appear on most dishes, es-pecially plastic ware. These can be re-moved in the dishwasher using the following procedure. Remove all met-alware from the dishwasher; load the stained cups, glasses, or dishes; fill the detergent cup with detergent; pour one teaspoon of chlorine bleach over the detergent in the cup; operate dishwasher through all cycles. *Re-peated* use of chlorine bleach in the dishwasher may be harmful to the dishes and some of the rubber parts of the machine. Limiting its use to once a month should be enough to control staining.

A concentration of manganese and iron in the wash water can produce dark brown stains on the nylon or plastic parts of the dishwasher. The stains can be removed by putting up to a teaspoon of citric acid crystals in the detergent cup during a wash. If citric acid is difficult to obtain in small quantities, strong unsweetened lemon juice can be used.

Gray or black marks on dinnerware after a wash are almost always caused by contact with aluminum.

Since there are no aluminum parts in the dishwasher itself, these marks can only be created by aluminum utensils in the wash. To prevent such stains from occurring, separate the dishes from the aluminum pieces when loading the machine. To remove the stains, rub with baking soda or chlorine bleach and follow with a thorough wash and rinse.

Aluminum ware should be placed in the dishwasher where it will not be sprinkled with undissolved detergent when the detergent cup opens. If alu-minum becomes discolored, the stain can be removed by scouring with a mild abrasive, then brightened by stacking the clean aluminum in the dishwasher and filling the detergent cup with cream of tartar. Run the dishwasher only through the wash cycle, then remove the aluminum ware and polish it with soap-filled steel-wool pads.

Much of the flatware manufactured today is made of stainless steel. It re-sists staining and corrosion because of the presence of chromium and, to a lesser degree, nickel in the alloy. The oxides of these elements form a tightly adhering transparent film on the steel surface of the flatware to protect it from corrosion. Salt, vinegar, fruit, fruit juices, tomatoes, milk, and milk products can cause breaks in the oxide film. A small salt crystal left on a piece of flatware may leave a pitted spot. Dry detergent poured directly on flatware can cause pitting or corrosion, as can cleaning with an abrasive cleanser. At the time the film is broken the spot may be too small to see, but it will eventually become larger and more evident.

Pitting and discoloration are two different corrosive processes. Pitting will occur only if there is a break in the protective oxide film. Discoloration, usually to bluish-black, also results from food left on flatware, but it does not necessarily entail a break in the oxide film. It can be removed by hand washing with a detergent solution and then thoroughly rinsing and drying. Both pitting and discoloration can be kept at a minimum or eliminated completely if food is always rinsed off properly.

A high iron content in the water supply can create rust spots. These usually appear in the bowls of spoons and along the cutting edges of knives. To remove them, soak the silverware in a mild solution of citric acid and hot water, then rinse and dry thoroughly.

Silver flatware requires extra care and protection. It is subject to tarnish from food, alkaline products, and fumes. Sulfide tarnish is most common and comes from contact with eggs, seafood, mayonnaise, and other foods containing sulfides. (Silver should not be stored near rubber, which is high in sulfur.) The tarnish starts out yellow, gradually darkens to a deep brown, and eventually becomes almost black-brown. It can be removed with silver polish.

Dishwashing detergent or household bleach that is allowed to remain on silver will also produce a black tarnish. It may appear as specks, blotches, or streaks. An overloaded silverware basket prevents water from circulating properly and causes moist detergent to remain in contact with the silver. The black tarnish that results can be removed with silver polish.

Silver-plated flatware showing worn spots should *never* be placed in the dishwasher with other flatware. Silver has a strong tendency to establish electrolysis in the water, which transfers the exposed copper behind the silver plating to all other metals and gives them a yellow tarnish which can be removed only with silver polish.

Silver must be completely dry before storing. If it is not used often, it should be wrapped in Pacific cloth or put in a chest lined with the same material. The cloth is widely used by jewelers and is available in most department stores.

Milky-white film left on glassware after a wash, particularly in hard-water areas or where reduced-phosphate detergents (those containing less than 12 percent phosphorus) are used, is created by calcium that has combined with the phosphate. When there is enough detergent present, the calcium will be kept soluble and flushed out. If the amount is insufficient, some of the calcium salt will precipitate and create a film which is deposited throughout the dishwasher but is first noticed on the glassware.

In soft water, there is little or no calcium and consequently no film. As little as $\frac{1}{3}$ to $\frac{1}{2}$ cup of detergent is sufficient when the water hardness is between 0 and 3 grains. As the water becomes harder, the amount of calcium and magnesium increases, and more detergent is required to keep the calcium soluble. A full cup or even $1\frac{1}{2}$ cups of a low-phosphate detergent is necessary in hard water (10 grains or more). The simplest way to remedy the situation is to keep adding slightly more detergent to each successive wash until the film disappears.

In stubborn cases, or where the tub and door show heavy deposits of calcium, the use of citric acid crystals is recommended. Some manufacturers stock citric acid as part of a cleaning kit complete with instructions.

Etching in glassware is the removal of metal ions from the glass. Once removed, they cannot be replaced. The lack of minerals in soft water sometimes causes etched glassware. An alkaline wash solution or insufficient rinsing, which leaves detergent and other material on the glass, will also cause glassware to become etched. The amount of detergent should be greatly reduced in soft water. Exactly how much is optimum should be determined by gradually reducing the amount of detergent until a satisfactory wash is obtained.

To determine whether your problem is etching or filming, pour a small quantity of vinegar into a defective glass. Wash inside and out. Rinse and dry the glass. If the film is gone, it was caused by calcium (tripolyphosphate). If the film returns to the completely dried glass, it is etching. The etched glass cannot be restored to its original condition.

Water containing excessive iron is another common culprit. This is particularly prevalent in areas where the iron content is 10 or more parts per million. (Usually water contains approximately 1 part per million.) As the colorless iron in the water is oxidized by contact with air, reddish-brown rust is produced (occasionally the rust will be yellow, yellow-brown, or tan). Fairly soft water may have a high iron content, but high concentrations are found more often in hard water.

When staining occurs because of the iron content in wash water, it is advisable to use a conditioning detergent that will hold the iron in suspension and prevent it from forming deposits. Reducing the water temperature to 150°F at the sink water tap will also help; the hotter the water, the greater the precipitation of iron.

To remove the iron film, wash the dishes as usual with detergent but stop the machine before it goes into the drying cycle. Place two heaping teaspoons of oxalic acid crystals in the detergent cup and rewash the dishes. (When using oxalic acid, chlorine bleach, or vinegar in a dishwasher, be sure to remove silverware, cutlery, or metal utensils first, as these solutions will corrode such items.) Once again, omit the drying cycle. Follow with a third wash using a full cup of detergent to wash away all traces of oxalic acid. Repeat the acid wash to remove especially heavy film deposits. A note of caution: *Oxalic acid is poisonous.* When used to remove iron film or stains, it must be completely washed away afterward. It must also be kept away from children and stored in a location where it will not be mistaken for food.

6

ELECTRIC STOVES

The General Electric stove shown in Figure 133 is used for most of the repairs discussed in this chapter. The top is removed by unfastening the two retaining screws located at the back, lifting the rear slightly, then pushing the top forward until it clears the two retaining prongs underneath the front edge.

SITUATION A:
You switch on a burner and get no heat. All other burners work properly.

This common malfunction is usually caused by a defective switch or heating element. Other possible but less likely causes are loose or broken wires or corroded terminals. You should first examine the sheath.

Pictured in Figure 134 is a defective *Calrod*. The arrow points to a rupture in its protective outer sheath, a thin tube made of an iron, nickel, and chrome alloy that resists oxidation and deterioration at the high temperatures common in electric ranges. Ruptures usually result from abuse, not normal usage.

A helical resistance wire made of a nickel and chrome alloy called *nichrome* is centered inside the Calrod. The flow of electricity through this wire encounters resistance which converts the electricity to heat. The Calrod is packed with magnesium oxide, which carries the heat from the nichrome wire to the sheath while providing the necessary electrical insulation.

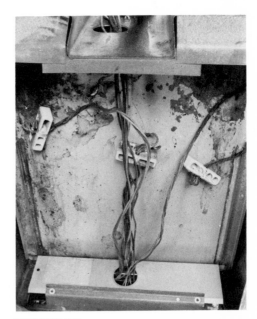

FIGURE 133

FIGURE 134

FIGURE 135

Once the sheath is ruptured, the Calrod should be discarded. The break in Figure 134 occurred when baking soda was accidentally spilled on a nick in the sheath. The Calrod was "on" at the time, and the baking soda ate its way through the sheath.

An intact sheath does not always mean that the Calrod is effective; there may still be a break in the nichrome wire. Before attempting to remove the Calrod for testing, unplug the appliance cord. *In all tests performed on an electric range, power to the unit must be cut off.*

The Calrod can be attached in one of two ways. A plug-in Calrod is removed by lifting it slightly and pulling straight up from a hinged receptacle. (The plug-in receptacle assembly is mounted with one screw and can be serviced by removing the screw and pulling the receptacle through the opening in the stove top.)

Figure 135 shows the other type, a retaining-screw Calrod, which is detached by removing the screw located in the circumference of the cutout portion of the stove top. Lift out the burner and its ceramic insulator.

The terminals of the Calrod are attached by screws to the insulator block shown in Figure 136. Remove the screws and lift out the Calrod.

Pictured in Figure 137 are the ends of a typical Calrod. Because of the high heat to which it is subjected, the assembly is mounted in ceramic. To test the Calrod, prepare the continuity tester and place its probes as shown in Figures 138 and 139.

In the first test (Figure 138), one probe is placed against the single terminal farthest to the left and the other on the double terminal at the opposite end of the burner. In the second test (Figure 139), the probe on the left is shifted to the single terminal in the center while the other remains in place. (Do not use a buzzer for these tests—too little current will come through to sound it, even if the Calrod is intact.) *Both* tests must indicate continuity or the burner is defective and must be replaced.

Calrods are manufactured in 6- and 8-inch diameters, single- and two-coil, spot heat and interwound. Be sure that the replacement is a duplicate of the original Calrod.

If the Calrod is found operational and before proceeding to test the switch, examine the ends of the lead wires (usually 16-gauge stranded

FIGURE 136

FIGURE 137

FIGURE 138

FIGURE 139

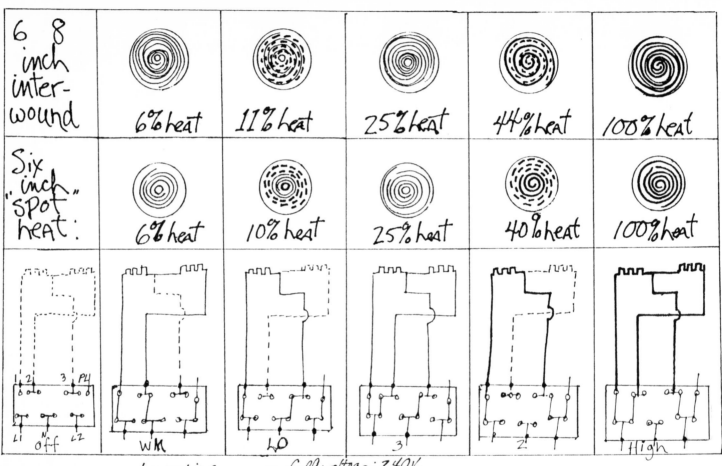

FIGURE 140

wire with special heat-resistant insulation). If these wires are nicked or over-compressed, high electrical resistance will be produced when they are crimped to the terminals, creating excessive heat, which will eventually fracture the wire.

If the wires feel brittle or appear broken, cut off the defective sections. Strip about $\frac{1}{2}$ inch of insulation, solder the wire strands together, form a loop around the terminal screw, and tighten the screw, making sure the wire loop does not overlap and turns in the same direction as the screw. (This is preferable to crimping a connector to the end of the wire.)

If the wires and Calrod are functional, the controlling switch should be tested next. Figure 140 shows what happens to the Calrod when the switch that controls it is placed in each of its various positions. To get at the switch, first pull off all knobs on the front panel (see Figure 141). This will expose the pairs of screws which attach each switch to the panel.

Two additional screws fasten the entire panel to the frame of the stove (see Figure 142). One is located in the lower-left corner and the other in the lower-right corner. Remove them to free the panel. (To allow the panel to

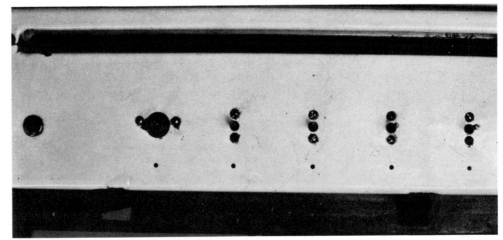

FIGURE 141

FIGURE 142

FIGURE 143

FIGURE 144

slip off the switch shafts, and for convenience during testing, remove all the switch-attachment screws.)

Pictured in Figure 143 are the switches behind the panel. On this model, the first three from the left control the burners on top of the stove; the fourth switch controls the oven and broiler elements and operates in conjunction with a thermostat. To test a specific switch, first remove a lead from one of its two terminals and replace the knob, matching the D-shape in its hub with the same shape on the shaft. Place the switch in the OFF position. Prepare the continuity tester and place its probes on the switch terminals as shown in Figure 144. No continuity should be evidenced. Rotate the knob through all the "on" positions. If no continuity is still evidenced, the switch is defective and must be replaced.

To replace the defective switch, detach its leads (the two mounting screws have already been removed), and install a new switch by reattaching the leads, the two mounting screws, the two screws which attach the control panel, and finally the knob.

If both the switch and Calrod are

functional, and there is no break in
the wires around the terminals, the
only remaining possible defect (it does
not happen very often) is a break or
loose connection in the wires that
supply electricity to the burner.

Figure 145 shows the back of the
stove. The appliance cord enters in
the center of the stove at the bottom
of a long vertical U-shaped depression which is covered with a strip of
sheet metal. To get at the wires and
their terminals, detach a screw on
each side of the strip and tap it upward until it clears the remaining
tabs.

When the cover strip is removed, a
portion of the wires and their back
terminals will be exposed, as shown
in Figure 146. Removing the top of
the stove will expose the remainder of
the wires and their front terminals. It
is now possible to trace each wire
from beginning to end.

Start at the Calrod terminal and
follow the wire to its back terminal. If
no break is seen, detach the wire from
both terminals. Prepare the continuity tester and place a probe at each
end of the wire. If continuity is evidenced, the wire is all right. If no continuity is evidenced, the wire is defective and is causing the malfunction.

FIGURE 145

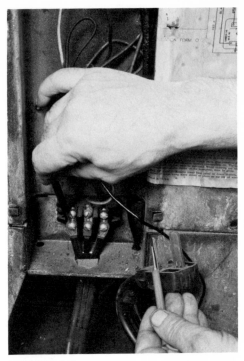

FIGURE 146

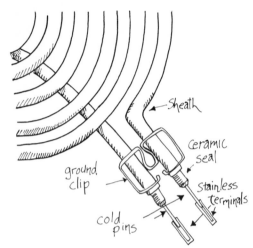

FIGURE 147

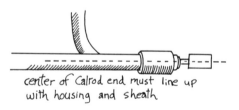

center of Calrod end must line up
with housing and sheath

FIGURE 148

Replace the wire and attach the ends of the new wire to the appropriate terminals. (Soldered ends are preferable to crimped connectors because of the high voltage involved.) If the first wire evidences continuity, repeat the same test on each remaining wire until the defective one is found.

If a plug-in surface terminal is difficult to insert or remove, look at the male terminals. They should have parallel sides with no outward bow.

To straighten a terminal, squeeze it with a pair of pliers until the distance between the cold pins (see Figure 147) is the same as the width of the loop in the ground clip. Do not pinch the ends of the terminals or the loop will be deformed. Make sure the male terminals are parallel and are perpendicular to the ground clip. They should also be perfectly in line with the straight ends of the sheath. (Take care not to damage the ceramic seal pictured in Figure 148.)

The center flanges or projecting tips of the ground clip should be bent in at a 90-degree angle. They should not touch. Use a pair of long-nosed pliers to bend the flanges.

Do not alter the unit terminals or ground clips except as described above or you may create a hazardous condi-

tion. Be especially careful not to touch the contact springs in the receptacle or the lead-in grounding flanges of the receptacle bracket.

SITUATION B:
You set the oven temperature-control dial at a certain temperature, say 375°F. The recipe calls for two hours of baking time at this temperature. It takes much longer for the dish to be baked.

This condition is usually caused by a thermostat in need of adjustment or an oven door that doesn't close properly.

To adjust the thermostat, you must first determine what the actual temperature is with the dial set at 375°F. A thermocouple type of thermometer does this most accurately. If you have one available, place the oven rack in its center position and clip the thermocouple to the middle of the rack. Run its leads out through the bottom of the door at the hinge and close the door. Place the tester on the floor next to the range. Turn the oven switch to BAKE and set the control knob to 375°F.

Wait 20 minutes, then watch until the temperature-cycle light goes on.

Record the oven temperature. When the light goes off, the cycle will have reached its highest temperature. Record it. Compute the average temperature—if the light went on at 310° and off at 420°, the average would be 365°F. The acceptable average temperature when the knob is set at 375° is between 355° and 395°F.

Figure 149 shows the back of the thermostat knob. The screw fastens a metal plate with a pointer positioned over a marked scale. Each mark usually represents 10°F, but this can vary in different models.

If the average temperature recorded is, say, 365°F, loosen the screw, move the pointer one mark to the left, and tighten the screw. This will raise the oven temperature 10°F.

Maximum knob adjustment is +20° or −30°F. A thermostat that cannot be adjusted over at least a 40° range should be replaced.

If no thermocouple is available to measure the temperature, an approximate reading can be made with a meat thermometer placed on a brick on the center rack or hung by a wire from any rack so that it does not touch any of the oven walls. Wait about 20 minutes. Read the high and

low temperatures at the beginning and end of several cycles. Average the readings and make any necessary adjustment.

Occasionally, the hub of the thermostat dial becomes so worn that there is play between the knob and the thermostat shaft. If this happens, pull off the knob and replace it.

Most oven thermostats in non-self-cleaning ovens have a control mechanism which provides remote sensing through a capillary tube in the oven. The tube actuates a lever system in the thermostat which makes or breaks the circuit to the oven.

If the capillary tube lies against the oven liner or is less than ¾ inch from the heating element, it will record unduly high temperatures. This will prematurely shut off power to the heating element and the oven will operate at too low a temperature.

The capillary is held by clips mounted to the liner wall. If it lies too close to the element, bend the clips with pliers to widen the gap to at least ¾ inch. If the capillary tube rests against the liner, bend or reposition it so that no contact is made.

If the door doesn't shut properly, the temperature in the oven will be lower than indicated, since heat is at-

FIGURE 149

FIGURE 150

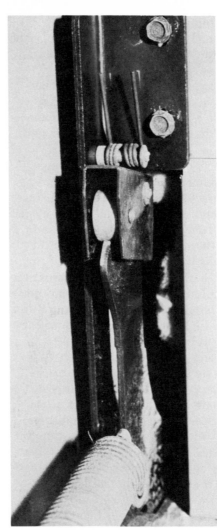

FIGURE 151

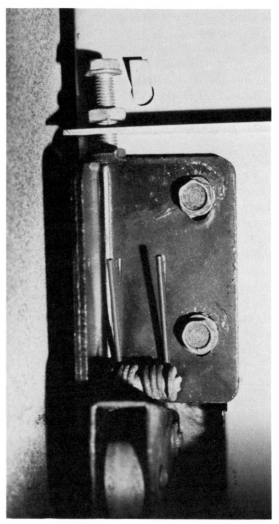

FIGURE 152

tracted by cold and the hot air in the oven will move toward the cooler air of the room.

A gap is normally left along the bottom on the oven door to allow for expansion of the oven liner, lest the top of the door be forced open as the temperature rises. Even so, after long periods of use, most doors will no longer shut perfectly, and for this reason all manufacturers provide methods of adjustment.

Pictured in Figure 150 is a portion of the spring that keeps the door closed. It is located under the stove with one end attached to the oven's frame. Figure 151 shows the opposite end of the spring, attached to the hinge mechanism.

A close view of the adjusting mechanism, composed of a threaded bolt and two nuts, is given in Figure 152. To adjust the door, first lay the stove on its back. Turn the bottom nut on the bolt counterclockwise to back it off, then turn the bolt clockwise until the nut is seated tightly against the hinge bracket. This will place greater tension on the spring and fit the door more tightly against the oven opening. (Reverse the procedure if the door lies too tightly against the opening.)

There is no way to determine just how much additional tension should be placed on the spring to make the door close properly. It is best to try a small adjustment at first, then swing the door to see if it closes properly. Make more small adjustments as needed until the door remains in an upright position.

In-out and up-down adjustment of the door can be made in some units by adjusting the hex-head screws shown in Figure 153. Remove the spring and loosen the screws, reposition the door, then retighten the screws and reattach the spring.

SITUATION C:
Sometimes food burns in the oven; other times food must be cooked longer than usual.

This condition is almost always caused by a defective thermostat or a thermostat capillary that has been knocked out of its retaining clips and is making intermittent contact with the liner wall or heating element. Look at the capillary. If it is properly positioned, the thermostat needs replacement.

To remove a defective thermostat, first pull all knobs off the control

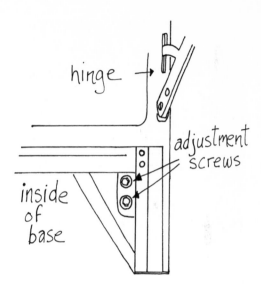

FIGURE 153

panel. Detach the pairs of screws that attach the switches to the panel. Remove the two side screws that attach the panel to the oven, then remove the panel. Detach the thermostat leads. Lift the capillary out of its retaining clips. Install a new thermostat by reversing the procedure.

SITUATION D:
You turn the selector switch to BAKE but the element does not heat.

FIGURE 154

This malfunction may be caused by a defective switch, a defective thermostat, or a defective heating element.

Remove the switch as previously described and place a probe of the continuity tester on each of its terminals. Turn the knob to BAKE. If continuity is evidenced, the switch is all right. If no continuity is evidenced, the switch is defective and must be replaced.

If the switch is functioning properly, detach a lead from the thermostat and place a probe on each of its terminals. Rotate the knob through all "on" positions. If continuity is evidenced, the thermostat is effective. If no continuity is evidenced, replace the thermostat.

If both switch and thermostat are functional, test the bake element. To remove the element, unfasten the screws that hold the element-support brackets located at the bottom and rear of the oven. Detach the element terminals from the ceramic insulator and remove the element. Prepare the continuity tester and test the bake element using the procedure previously described for the surface element. If no continuity is evidenced, replace the bake element by reversing the procedure just described.

SITUATION E:
A plug-in Calrod will not lie flat.

This problem usually occurs when the Calrod has been raised beyond its normal hinge swing. To correct the condition, remove the Calrod, the trim ring, and the reflector pan. Reach through the opening and push up the back part of the receptacle as far as possible. Replace the reflector pan and trim ring. Insert the Calrod, keeping it as close to the cooktop as you can until its supports fall within the trim ring. Place your palm flat on top of the Calrod, exerting a downward force while sliding the unit toward the receptacle until it is positioned in the trim ring.

SITUATION F:
Both surface burners on one side fail to operate.

This situation arises when one of the two hot wires that supply electricity to the burners become defective. Pictured in Figure 154 are the ends of the three wires in the appliance cord connected to their terminals in the insulated ceramic block. The white center wire is the neutral or ground wire. The black and red wires on either side of it are the hot wires. One of them has lost continuity and is causing the dead burners.

Stoves use both 120 and 240 volts–120 volts when either the red *or* black wire is used in conjunction with the white neutral wire, and 240 volts when both the red *and* black wires are used.

Figure 155 diagrams the typical wiring arrangement in an electric stove. The arrangement varies slightly in different models, but the essential aspects are the same for all units. (Every unit comes with a drawing of its wiring.)

Directly above the three appliance-cord terminals are the three terminals pictured in Figure 156. They are the point of departure for all the wiring that continues to the various components of the stove–really only a convenient extension of the lead-in appliance cord.

The appliance cord on an electric stove is made of heavy-duty materials more than adequate to carry the high voltages that operate the stove. Stoves are rarely shifted about and there is little probability of a break developing in the appliance cord. It is therefore *unlikely* that any malfunction can be traced to the appliance cord.

Unlike other appliances, which are often simply plugged into an existing outlet, a stove is wired directly in a junction box. Three #6 wires, fused at 60 amps, are usually used. The wires are connected directly to the main and there are no other appliances on the circuit. The fuses rarely blow, and only when all other potential malfunctions have been investigated should the house wiring or appliance cord be examined.

With the control panel on top of the stove and the cover strip over the U-shaped depression at the rear of the stove removed, all wires to all terminals will be completely exposed. Lift the red wire attached to the terminal block at the rear of the stove and trace it to its first terminal connection at the front. Detach one end from the terminal and prepare the multitester. Place a probe on each end of the wire. If continuity is not evidenced, the wire is defective even if a break cannot be seen. If continuity is evidenced, continue to trace the red wire to its terminal connections on the inoperative burners. Repeat the continuity test between terminals. If any test reveals a loss of continuity in the red wire, it is defective and must be replaced. If the red wire reveals conti-

nuity all along its path, repeat the same continuity tests on the black wire.

Any replacement wire should be #16 with an asbestos insulation. This can be purchased at a hardware or appliance store. The new terminal connections *should not* be made with crimped-on connectors (although this is the method usually used in the factory, a nonprofessional is too likely to do an imperfect job of installing crimped connectors).

To make any new connections, strip approximately $\frac{1}{2}$ inch of insulation from the end of the wire, place the tip of a soldering gun against the bare wire until the wire is hot enough to melt rosin-core solder (acid-core solder should not be used in electrical connections), and deposit the solder along the stripped wire. Allow it to cool, then form the soldered wire into a U just wide enough to fit under the terminal screw. Position the looped wire so that it will turn inward as the screw is tightened clockwise.

SITUATION G:
Fluorescent light doesn't work.

This usually results from a defective switch, a defective ballast, an improp-

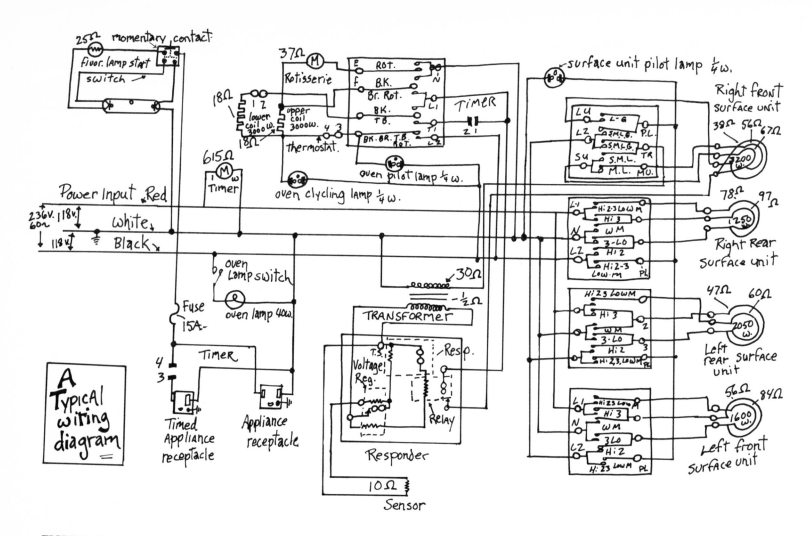

FIGURE 155

FIGURE 156

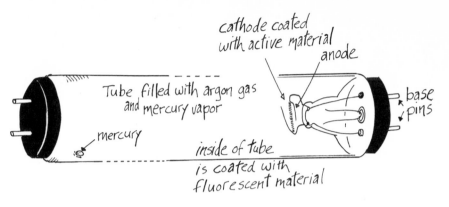

cathode coated
with active material
anode
Tube filled with argon gas
and mercury vapor
base
pins
mercury
inside of tube
is coated with
fluorescent material

FIGURE 157

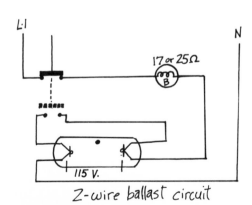

L·1
N
17 or 25 Ω
B
115 V.
2-wire ballast circuit

FIGURE 158

erly spaced receptacle, or a faulty fluorescent tube.

Figure 157 shows the construction of a typical fluorescent lamp. When the switch is pushed on, two sets of contacts come together and establish continuity through the switch. One set of contacts provides the initial start and the other set continues to supply electricity.

The starting contacts are on a separate circuit (see Figure 158), which contains the preheated filaments and ballast. As the push-button switch is released, the starting contacts open to form an arc inside the lamp. Ultraviolet radiation is created. The phosphor-coated tube absorbs the radiation and returns it as visible light. The mercury vapor inside the tube conducts electricity and maintains the continuity of the circuit throughout the tube.

Pictured in Figure 159 is a typical lamp switch. The red marks indicate the starting-circuit contacts. To test the switch, depress the push-button and place the probes of the continuity tester on the red terminals first and then on the two remaining ones. *Both* pairs of terminals must evidence continuity or the switch must be replaced.

If the switch evidences continuity, the ballast (shown in Figure 158) should be examined next.

The ballast provides the initial volt-

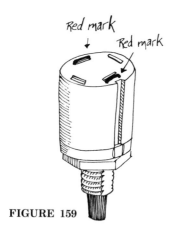

Red mark
Red mark

FIGURE 159

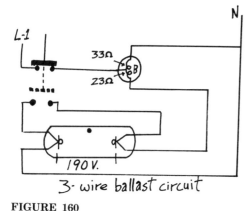

L-1
N
33Ω
23Ω
190 V.

3-wire ballast circuit

FIGURE 160

age needed to strike an arc between the filaments. It also limits the flow of current through the lamp once it has been started. (If the current is not regulated, it will continue to build up and eventually burn out the lamp.)

Lamps up to 25 watts use a 120-volt choke ballast. Any lamp over 30 watts uses a three-wire auto-transformer ballast (see Figure 160), which increases the voltage to about 190 volts.

To test the ballast, place a probe of the continuity tester on each of its terminals. Ballasts in lamps of 20 watts or less should give a reading around 25 ohms; with 25-watt lamps, you should get a reading of approximately 70 ohms. If markedly higher readings are obtained, or if no continuity is evidenced, replace the ballast. (To remove, push in and rotate counterclockwise; to install, push in, rotate clockwise, then release.)

In order for the terminals in the lamp receptacle to make pressure contact with the lamp terminal pins, the space between the pins must not be more than $\frac{1}{2}$ inch (see Figure 161). The pins must also be in the same plane so that contact is made in both sockets.

If the lamp is correctly positioned

in the receptacles, and the ballast and switch have been found functional but the distance between the lamp pins and the back of the sockets exceeds $\frac{1}{8}$ inch, replace the lamp. Figure 162 shows a correctly installed lamp. (The reason the lamp was not replaced before checking the ballast is that a defective ballast would have immediately caused it to burn out.)

SITUATION H:
Ceramic cooktop fails to operate.

Pictured in Figure 163 is the heating-element assembly used under a ceramic cooktop and its temperature control. Failure to operate may be due to any of the reasons previously given in this chapter or because the temperature control through which it operates may have become defective.

The control shown in Figure 164 is used in conjunction with each heating element assembly and provides a maximum temperature limit of about 900°F. It is attached to the assembly by a temperature sensor between the heater and the cooking panel. The sensor consists of a ceramic tube containing a metal rod, both of which are connected to a set of contacts that are normally closed. Electricity on its way

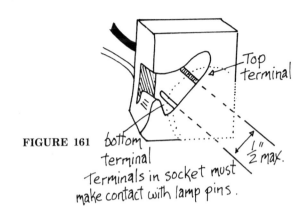

FIGURE 161

Top terminal

bottom terminal

$\frac{1}{2}$" max.

Terminals in socket must make contact with lamp pins.

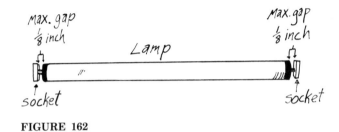

max. gap $\frac{1}{8}$ inch

Lamp

max. gap $\frac{1}{8}$ inch

socket

socket

FIGURE 162

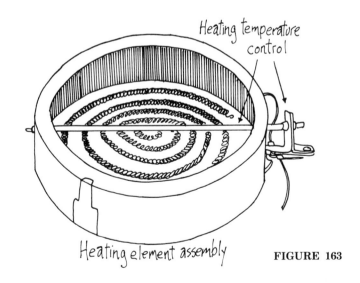

Heating temperature control

Heating element assembly

FIGURE 163

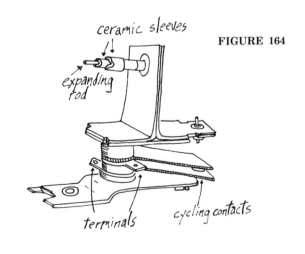

ceramic sleeves

FIGURE 164

expanding rod

terminals

cycling contacts

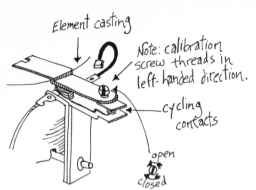

Element casting

Note: calibration screw threads in left-handed direction.

cycling contacts

open
closed

FIGURE 165

to the heater must first pass through the tube. As the temperature increases, the metal rod expands more quickly than the tube, opening the contacts and shutting off electricity to the heater. With power cut off, the rod cools, the contacts close, and another heating cycle begins.

A continuity test with probes on the terminals of the temperature control unit will determine whether or not it is defective.

A new control must be calibrated or adjusted. (If an element is replaced, or if the cooking panel breaks from high temperatures, the old but still functioning control must be recalibrated.)

To calibrate the control, place a high-temperature thermometer in the center of the control unit. Turn the heat switch to high. After about eight minutes, the maximum temperature should be 900°F (plus or minus 25°F).

To make an adjustment, use the calibration screw pictured in Figure 165. A one-eighth clockwise turn of the screw raises the indicated temperatures approximately 50°F on the small elements and 75°F on the large elements.

As with all repairs discussed in this chapter, disconnect the power before replacing a defective high-temperature unit. Remove the cooktop and lower the wiring guard from the heater box. Loosen the spring screws in the element retainer bar and remove the bar. Remove the element and defective control unit, calibrate it, then seal the calibration screw with epoxy thread sealer.

7

AUTOMATIC DRYERS

The typical electric dryer has a 120-volt, $\frac{1}{4}$-horsepower motor that turns at 1725 revolutions per minute and draws approximately 5.5 amps when drying a full load. It rotates a tub at approximately 50 revolutions per minute, using a pulley and belt. Baffles inside the tub cause the clothes to tumble. Heat is provided by two 240-volt heater coils behind the drum. A blower and connected ductwork pull air into the lower front of the cabinet and draw it up across the heaters. This hot air is then pulled through the rear of the tub and across the tumbling clothes, through the lint trap, and down the trap duct to the blower. It is then pushed out the exhaust by the blower. (See Figure 166.)

Many malfunctions occur because of excessive lint accumulation which restricts the air flow and causes unsatisfactory drying or breakdown of some part. Failure of electrical components, in particular the motor centrifugal switch (a safety device), is also a frequent problem, as are malfunctions caused by stretched or broken belts within the machine or foreign items such as bobby pins shorting out the heater coils.

Figure 167 shows the electrical wiring arrangement in a typical dryer. Engaging the safety switch when the timer is on (and the dial turned to the desired temperature or fabric type) starts the machine.

SITUATION A:

You load the machine, turn the selector switch to the desired position, place the timer dial on START, and shut

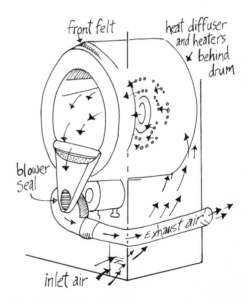

FIGURE 166

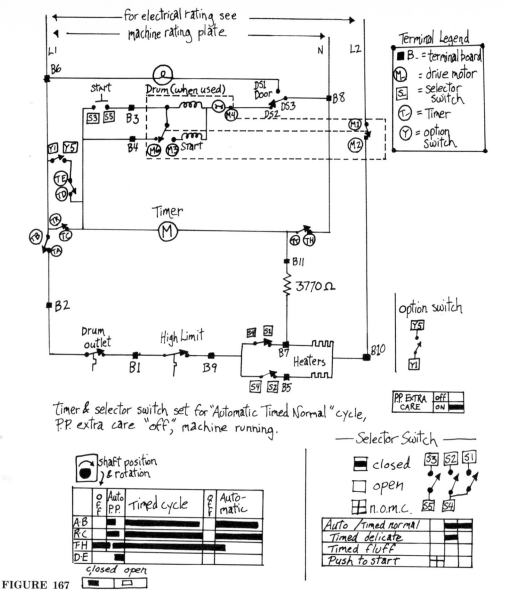

for electrical rating see
machine rating plate

L1
B6

start   Drum (when used)   DS1 Door   B8

S3 S5   B3   DS3
                DS2

Y1 Y5   B4   M6 M3 Start   M1 M2

TE
TD

TB TC
TA

Timer
M

TB TH

B11
3770 Ω

option switch
Y5

Y1

B2

Drum outlet   High Limit   S4 S1
B1   B9   B7 Heaters   B10

S4 S2 B5

Terminal Legend

■ B = terminal board
Ⓜ = drive motor
Ⓢ = selector switch
Ⓣ = Timer
Ⓨ = option switch

Timer & selector switch set for "Automatic Timed Normal" cycle,
P.P. extra care "off", machine running.

P.P. EXTRA CARE	off	
	ON	■

shaft position & rotation

	OFF	Auto P.P.	Timed cycle	OFF	Auto-matic
A·B					
R·C					
F·H					
D·E					

closed open

FIGURE 167   ■ □

— Selector Switch —

■ closed
□ open
⊞ n.o.m.c.

S3 S2 S1
S5 S4

Auto /Timed normal		
Timed delicate		
Timed fluff		
Push to start		

the machine door. (You engage the safety switch if there is one.) Nothing happens. The interior light in the dryer fails to go on when the door is open.

This malfunction may be caused by a defect in the house wiring, door switch, or appliance cord. A broken wire or loose terminal connection may also be at fault, but this is rare and should be investigated only after other possibilities have been eliminated.

To test the house wiring, first remove the appliance plug from its outlet. Pictured in Figure 168 is a typical 240-volt outlet. Each side slot is connected to the main by a separate 120-volt hot wire. The center slot is connected to the neutral white wire. (In some installations both the plug and outlet are replaced by a terminal block.)

Determine the voltage present in the outlet with a multitester. Position the selector knob to AC volts and insert a probe into each of the side slots of the plug. Read the voltage on the red AC scale. It should be between 220 and 240.

If a pigtail is used to test the outlet, place one of the leads in a side slot and the other in the center slot. If the bulb lights, 120 volts are present. Leave one lead in the center slot and shift the other to the opposite side. If the bulb illuminates again, it can be assumed that 240 volts are present and the cause of the malfunction lies elsewhere.

Electricity to the outlet is supplied from the main and controlled by fuses or breakers. If the outlet doesn't evidence 240 volts, replace the burned fuses or reset the breakers. If, with the dryer still unplugged, the new fuses blow or the breakers trip again, a short exists in the house wiring and has to be corrected by a professional. If the house wiring is functional, the door switch should be checked next.

The *door switch* pictured in Figure 169 is a typical push-button type. It is located near the door at the front of the dryer and is attached to the dryer frame with a locknut. When the door is open, the push-button is up, with its contacts closed to the interior light and open to the rest of the machine. When the door is shut and the push-button depressed, the switch contacts are open to the interior light and closed to the rest of the machine. When the interior light goes out, electricity is available as needed for all remaining components.

To obtain access to the switch, pull off the timer knob and unscrew the two Phillips screws. Remove the switch trim by pulling the right side forward. Unfasten the two screws and remove the control panel (shown in Figure 170) to gain access to the door switch. Removing the control panel will also provide access to the safety switch and timer.

To determine whether the door switch is operating, remove a lead from one of its terminals and prepare the continuity tester. Depress the push-button and place a probe of the tester on each of the switch terminals. (If there are four terminals, check each opposite pair with the button up and then down.) If continuity isn't evidenced, the switch is defective and must be replaced.

If the switch evidences continuity, next test the appliance cord. Unlike a 120-volt cord, the 240-volt cord contains two separate 120-volt hot wires. The white neutral wire should also evidence continuity regardless of the switched position. Both hot wires must evidence continuity or the appliance cord is defective.

To test the cord, trace the two hot wires from the point where they separate inside the dryer to their ends at

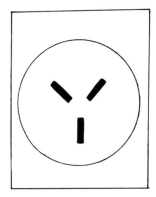

FIGURE 168

Switch is pushed in when door is shut.

FIGURE 169

Remove to service timer

FIGURE 170

the motor terminals. Prepare the continuity tester and place a probe on the end of either of the two hot wires. Place the second probe on either of the plug's two side prongs. If no continuity is evidenced, leave one probe on the wire end and shift the other to the opposite side prong. If again no continuity is evidenced, the cord is defective.

If the first test evidenced continuity, shift one probe to the end of the second wire and the other to the

plug's second side prong. If no continuity is evidenced, the appliance cord is defective and must be replaced.

SITUATION B:
You load the machine, set the selector switch at the desired temperature, rotate the timer dial to START, **shut the door, and engage the safety switch. Nothing happens.** *The interior light is on when the door is opened.*

The malfunction may be caused by a defective timer, safety switch, high-limit thermostat, centrifugal motor switch, or inoperative motor. The fact that the light goes on when the door is opened indicates that power is being delivered to the dryer and it can be assumed that the door switch, appliance cord, and house wiring are all right. (In rare cases, when only one of the hot wires lacks power, the malfunction will have to be determined and corrected as described in the previous section.)

To test the *timer,* trace the lead going from the motor terminal to the outgoing connection on the timer. Detach the lead from the timer prong. Attach one alligator clip from the buzzer tester to the prong. Attach the

second alligator clip to the timer's incoming hot-wire terminal. (You can identify the terminal by following the hot-wire lead to its connection on the timer.) Switch on the tester and rotate the timer dial. Buzzing should occur almost continuously throughout the rotation. If continuity is not evidenced, the timer is defective and must be replaced.

A lamp or multitester can be used in place of the buzzer to determine if the timer is operational. The procedure is exactly the same except that continuity is evidenced by a light bulb or a reading on the ohm scale.

Remove the defective timer by detaching all its push-on leads and unfastening the two mounting screws. The leads are color-coded and match the colors indicated beside the timer prongs. Reattach all the leads to the corresponding prongs on the new timer, use the screws removed earlier to remount the timer to the dryer, and replace the control panel, cover trim, and timer dial.

If the timer is all right, next check the safety switch beside it. Detach a lead from one of its terminals, prepare the continuity tester, place a probe on each of its terminals, and move the switch to the ON position. If no continuity is evidenced on the ohm scale, the switch is defective and must be replaced.

The *centrifugal switch* pictured in Figure 171 is one of the dryer's safety devices. It is positioned between the motor and heaters and is normally open. It prevents the heaters from coming on when the motor isn't running. As the motor reaches a preset number of revolutions per minute, the switch contacts close and electricity flows to the heaters.

To obtain access to the switch, remove the two screws at the bottom of the lower panel, 2 inches in from each side. Open the dryer door and lift off the panel. Remove the three screws

FIGURE 171

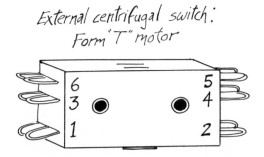

External centrifugal switch: Form "T" motor

from the service panel beneath it, then remove the panel.

The centrifugal switch (as well as the idler system and motor pulley) is now exposed. To test the switch, install a jumper wire between terminals 1 and 2 to bypass the switch and provide current directly to the motor. Attempt to start the machine. If the motor runs, the switch is defective and must be replaced. But first, while the motor is running, an additional continuity check should be performed on the switch by placing the leads of the test lamp on terminals 1 and 2. The bulb should go on if continuity is present and will go off when the motor stops.

If the centrifugal switch is operational, the *high-limit thermostat,* another safety device shown in Figure 172, should be checked. The switch shuts off power to the heaters when the temperature gets excessive and reestablishes continuity when the heat is reduced to operating temperature. The dryer can develop excessive temperatures from a variety of causes, but the most common is excessive lint accumulation.

To obtain access to the thermostat, remove the service panel in the rear

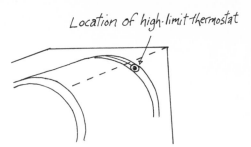

Location of high-limit thermostat

FIGURE 172

upper-left corner of the dryer. To test it, detach a lead and place the probes on the continuity tester on each of its terminals. If the thermostat is at room temperature and no continuity is evidenced, it is defective and must be replaced. If continuity is evidenced, further testing of the thermostat must be made to see if it is interrupting power to the heaters when necessary.

To test the high-limit thermostat, set the timer and selector switches on the empty dryer to HIGH HEAT. Open the door, depress the push-button switch, and start the dryer. Look at the heaters behind the drum. Measure the time from when the dryer starts until the thermostat clicks off or the heaters begin to lose their bright red color. The following table indicates normal operating times for the thermostat.

Room Temperature (Degrees Fahrenheit)	Tripping Time (Seconds)
100	51–80
90	53–83
80	55–86
70	56–91
60	59–97
50	64–106

If the heaters fail to go on or if the tripping time varies markedly from the figures given, the thermostat is defective and must be replaced.

In some machines a fuse is substituted for the high-limit thermostat. A simple continuity test will determine if it is working properly. Consult the wiring diagram in the dryer to locate the fuse.

Pictured in Figures 173, 174, and 175 are three typical motors used in dryers. They are permanently lubricated and have automatic-reset overload protectors.

The simplest method of testing a motor is to detach its leads and connect the direct-start cord to its terminals. The cord is then plugged into a 120-volt outlet and the switch turned

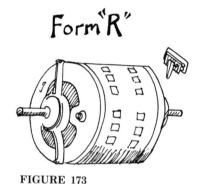

FIGURE 173

FIGURE 174

FIGURE 175

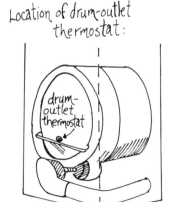

FIGURE 176

on for no more than a few seconds. If the motor runs, it is operational; if it fails to start it is defective.

A more complicated but equally valid method of testing the motor is to unplug the machine, detach the leads from the motor, and place the probes of the continuity tester on the terminals marked C (Common) and S (Start). If continuity is evidenced, switch the probe from the S terminal to the one marked R (Run). Leave the other probe on the C terminal. If continuity is not evidenced in *both* the starting and running positions, the motor is defective and must be replaced.

If continuity is shown in both positions, scrape some paint from a small area on the motor housing until bare metal is exposed. Place one probe on the bare metal and the other on the S terminal. *If continuity is evidenced, the motor is internally grounded and must be replaced.* If no continuity is evidenced, leave the probe on the bare metal and shift the other probe to the R terminal. Again, if continuity is evidenced, the motor must be replaced. Unless both these tests show a *lack* of continuity, the motor is defective and must be replaced.

SITUATION C:
Clothes take an abnormally long time to dry.

This is usually caused by excessive lint accumulation and less frequently by a defective drum-outlet thermostat. It will often be accompanied by hotter than normal temperatures.

Accumulated lint restricts the free flow of hot air through the ductwork. Less heat is available to dry the clothes. Simultaneously, pockets of excessively hot air develop around the thermostats. This causes both the high-limit thermostat and the drum-outlet thermostat to shut off the heaters prematurely.

A short-term solution is to disassemble the ductwork and remove the accumulated lint. The only way to avoid the problem is to remove all lint from the lint trap before *every* load. This is normal and necessary operating procedure. Omitting it will inevitably result in unsatisfactory drying and possibly in serious component failure.

If excessive lint does not prove to be the cause, the *drum-outlet thermostat* should be checked. Located under the lint trap as pictured in Figure 176, it

controls the heaters, turning them on when heat is required and off when the required temperature has been reached. It is positioned in the electrical circuit before the heaters, so that if the thermostat becomes defective with its contacts open, no electricity will flow to the heaters and no heat will be produced. To determine if this has occurred, detach a lead from the thermostat and place one probe of the multitester on each of its terminals. If no continuity is evidenced, the thermostat is defective and must be replaced.

Remove the lint trap pictured in Figure 177 to gain access to the defective thermostat. If the thermostat evidences continuity it may be operational, but not necessarily operating correctly. It may show continuity and still provide too little or too much heat, both of which will result in unsatisfactory drying.

In commercial repairs, a thermocouple is used to record temperatures when testing a thermostat. An oven thermometer can be substituted, and while the results will only be approximate, they should be accurate enough to indicate a defective thermostat.

To perform the test, place the ther-

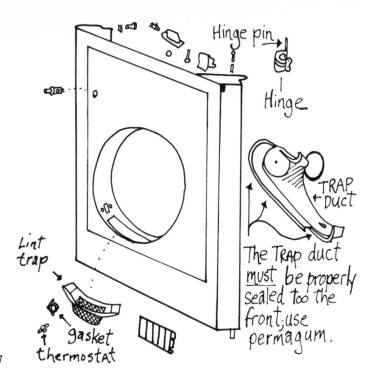

Hinge pin

Hinge

TRAP
Duct

Lint
trap

The TRAP duct
must be properly
sealed too the
front; use
permagum.

gasket
thermostat

FIGURE 177

If the temperatures observed vary markedly from the figures given above, coupled with unsatisfactory drying, the thermostat should be replaced.

SITUATION D:
No heat is produced in the machine.

Pictured in Figure 178 is a typical heater circuit. As can be seen from the drawing, the failure of the motor centrifugal switch, the selector switch, the timer, the drum-outlet thermostat, or the high-limit thermostat will result in a loss of heat. Access to and testing of each of these electrical components has been previously detailed (the same for both switches). Only after all parts have been found functional should the heaters themselves be tested. They fail much less frequently than the other components.

Two identical *heater coils* provide the dryer with heat. (Newer machines sometimes have Calrods instead.) The coils are operated together or separately, depending on the position of the selector switch; HIGH HEAT activates both coils, LOW HEAT one coil, and FLUFF neither coil. A defective heater will most often have a visible

mometer in the center of the lint trap. Disconnect the exhaust by pulling the hose off the duct and begin with the dryer at room temperature. Start the machine and record the operating temperature several times. The following chart gives the thermostat's normal operating ranges.

Room Temperature (Degrees Fahrenheit)	Maximum Temperature (Degrees Fahrenheit)	Minimum Temperature (Degrees Fahrenheit)
60	165–194	83
70	169–202	86
80	176–208	93
90	183–210	98

break in the nichrome wire that creates heat by resisting the flow of electricity. The heater can also become defective if a bobby pin or similar metallic item causes the nichrome wire to short.

To test the heater, first expose the terminals in the upper portion of the dryer by removing the top of the machine. Some tops are removed by inserting a one-inch putty knife in the joint between the top and front panel near two hidden spring clips, usually about two inches in from each side and marked by slightly deeper depressions in the joint (Figure 179). The putty knife is pushed against the clips to release the front end. The top is then lifted a couple of inches and pushed toward the rear until it is completely released. Other machines require the removal of two screws at the rear before the top is pushed forward.

To test the heater after its terminals are exposed, detach a lead and place the tester probes on each of the terminals. If continuity is evidenced, the coil is all right. If no continuity is evidenced, the coil must be repaired or replaced.

To get at the defective coil or coils behind the drum, detach the surface

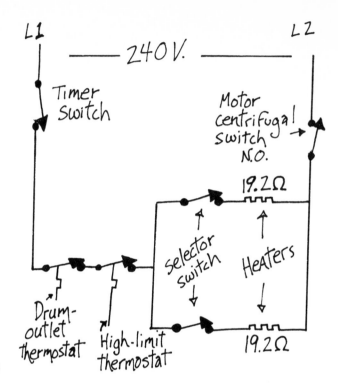

FIGURE 178

screws and remove the trim around the perimeter of the machine by sliding or lifting off each piece. Removing the trim will expose lines of perimeter screws. Remove them to free the panels. In some machines, the top and front are removed as pictured in Figures 179 and 180.

To remove the drum, first release the belt from the idler pulley. If the drum center has a plug-button cover, remove it and unscrew the ¾-inch nut behind it with a socket wrench. Pull the drum forward and lift it up and out. If there is no plug button, remove one mounting screw and drive it into

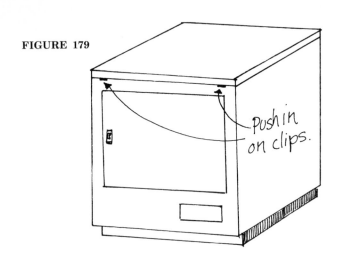

FIGURE 179

Push in on clips.

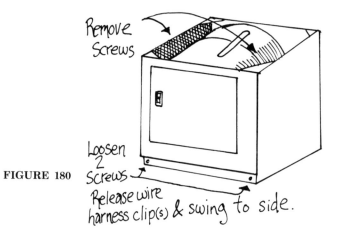

Remove Screws

Loosen 2 Screws

Release wire harness clip(s) & swing to side.

FIGURE 180

Heat deflector

Remove one screw and install in small tooling hole.

FIGURE 181

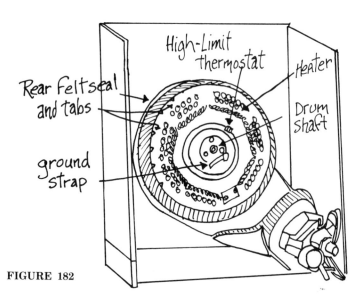

High-Limit thermostat

Heater

Drum Shaft

Rear Felt seal and tabs

ground strap

FIGURE 182

the drum fixture hole to secure the heat deflector to the drum as shown in Figure 181. Remove the two remaining drum-mounting screws and pull the drum forward, then up and out.

Figure 182 shows the dryer with the drum removed and coils exposed for mending or replacement. An examination of the coils will usually reveal what has caused the malfunction.

To remove and replace a defective coil, cut both ends of the coil at the terminals as pictured in Figure 183. Cut the end of the good coil only at the common terminal. Remove the two terminals from which the heater coils were cut and replace them with two new terminals (provided with the heater replacement kit).

Stretch the replacement coil to the correct length as shown in Figure 184. Remove the defective coil and thread the stretched replacement through the insulators. The coil should be evenly spaced to avoid creating hot spots. Form hooks on the ends of the coil with needle-nosed pliers and place the hooked ends on the terminals so that each is held between two washers as shown in Figure 185.

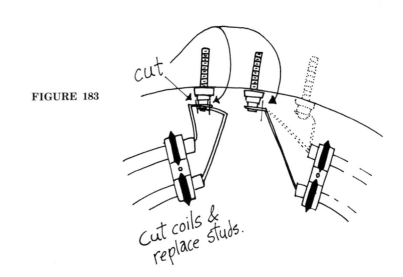

FIGURE 183

cut

Cut coils & replace studs.

FIGURE 184

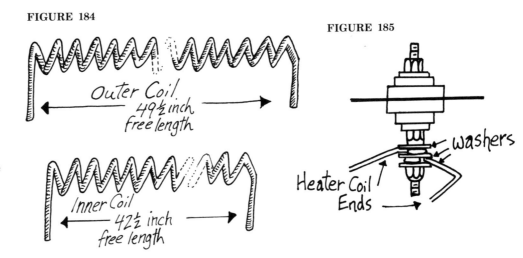

Outer Coil
49½ inch free length

Inner Coil
42½ inch free length

FIGURE 185

washers

Heater Coil Ends

FIGURE 186

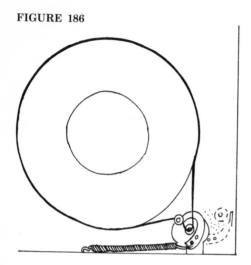

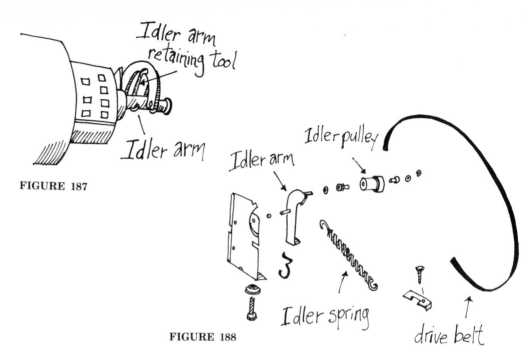

FIGURE 187

FIGURE 188

If the coil has a break, the ends can be joined with a mending sleeve. (Kits available from appliance dealers include adequate instructions.)

SITUATION E:
Drum fails to rotate.

This is a very common failure and is usually caused by a belt that is stretched and slipping, improperly po-sitioned, or broken. The drum will also fail to rotate if the door switch or motor is defective, but this is rare.

To test the switch and motor, in-stall a jumper wire across the switch terminals and start the machine. If the motor runs, the switch is defec-tive; if the motor doesn't run, the motor is defective.

If the motor is defective, examine both the rollers which support the drum and the Teflon slide on the back of the front panel for lint accumula-tion, which may have caused the drum to "freeze." In severe cases, a jammed tub will cause the motor to burn out. After the motor has been re-placed, lint should be cleaned away and the rollers lubricated until the tub spins freely so that the new motor doesn't suffer the same fate. Motor burnout is infrequent, however, and

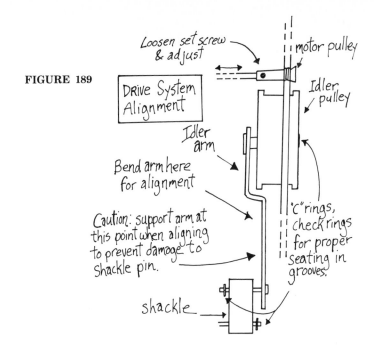

FIGURE 189

Loosen set screw & adjust

Drive System Alignment

motor pulley

Idler pulley

Idler arm

Bend arm here for alignment

Caution: support arm at this point when aligning to prevent damage to shackle pin.

"c" rings, check rings for proper seating in grooves.

shackle

the malfunction is usually caused by a defective belt.

To examine the belt and its operation, it is best to remove the top and rear access panels. If the belt is stretched or broken, remove it. Figure 186 shows the idler arm, belt, and motor shaft. The idler arm, whose function is to keep the belt taut, is under tension. When released from the belt, the arm will be pulled by the spring to the position shown in the drawing.

To install a new replacement belt, cock the idler arm as pictured in Figure 187. An idler-arm retainer tool can be purchased or formed from stiff wire. Position the new belt around the center of the drum. Put your left arm through the opening at the left drum glide and string the belt over the idler pulley and under and around the motor pulley. Remove the retainer tool by pushing the idler arm down and to the right.

A close examination of the idler assembly (shown in Figure 188) will reveal if the malfunction has been caused by a break in any of its parts.

If the belt is intact but has simply ridden off the rear of the motor pulley, it must be realigned. To check its operation, rotate the drum both clockwise and counterclockwise for several revolutions and observe the movement of the belt on the idler pulley. If the belt has tracked near the front or rear edge of the idler pulley, bend the idler arm as pictured in Figure 189 to center the belt.

SITUATION F:
No air is being blown through machine.

This may be caused by complete restriction in the duct system or, more likely, a motor made defective by excessive lint.

To remove the motor and blower, remove the drum, the motor leads, and the blower housing screws on the cabinet front. Release the rear motor mounting clip and remove and replace the assembly.

INDEX